A SHORT HISTORY OF SCIENCE

EDWIN P. HOYT

"A Short History
of Science"

Volume I—Ancient Science

ILLUSTRATED

The John Day Company
New York

© 1965 by Edwin P. Hoyt

*Library of Congress Catalogue
Card Number: 64-20704*

Contents

LIST OF ILLUSTRATIONS

A SHORT HISTORY OF SCIENCE

CHAPTER 1

Science in the Fertile Crescent

THE story of science is very much the story of
the growth of civilization in the world. Science as we
know it in the twentieth century is modern science and
dates from about the time of Galileo in the sixteenth and
seventeenth centuries. But modern science is the orchard
from which humanity picks the fruits. Its beginnings
were seeds sown in many lands.

Science began when men first used their brains to try
to solve problems. In the Pleistocene period, about a million years ago, the brains of the early men had developed
enough so that they were making tools. Here was a seed
of science. These early men knew fire. Other men learned
how to make fire when they wanted it, with tools. Still
others improved those tools. They were developing technology—an important part of science.

Technology developed slowly but steadily in many
ways. Men needed hammers, chisels, and knives to crush,

Acheulean flint hand axe

break, and slice. These were invented and made more efficient, and each improvement gave rise to new uses for the tools. In late Paleolithic times men applied mechanical principles to the use of tools. The bow was invented in this period and men used spear-throwers to increase the range of their weapons. At a time when men were developing language for spoken communication the tools they used showed the improvement of their cultures. These cultures varied, depending on the ways men used their minds. In Africa the bow became a standard weapon. In Australia ingenious primitive men developed the boomerang. Long before the beginning of recorded history, many of the seeds of science were sprouting, for these same men domesticated animals and learned to use animal products and plants as food and medicine. They performed surgical operations. Skulls that date back to the Stone Age period of 9000 B.C. show that ancient men were familiar with the surgical operation called trephination—the cutting of an opening through the top of the skull.

Since early men could not write, we do not know exactly when certain developments occurred. For example, the wheel was invented by prehistoric man, probably around the Black Sea or within the Fertile Crescent. Imagine what a difference the wheel made in man's way of life. Before the wheel men hauled animals and their belongings on crude sledges. They also used long poles bound together at one end, with the other end dragging along the ground. (Indians of the American plains still used that travois method of transportation in the nineteenth century.)

Would one call the development of the wheel a scientific attainment? It certainly was if we take the broad view of science, and say that science is the application of the mind to a problem, under controlled conditions. Then, we might say that Stone Age men who first learned to flake flint were scientists. Why not? They experimented, using the same materials and trying to cut them in different ways. They recorded their knowledge, passing it down in the hands and minds of other men. If we call this process early technology, which it really is, this is the dawning of science—the application of thought to a problem.

With the wheel, the sledge, and the travois, we can see that men solved their problems in some remarkable ways. The wheel is a masterpiece of invention. One can scarcely turn his head without seeing something in which wheels

are used, whether in a clock, the casters on a piece of furniture, an automobile, or the ribbon spool of a typewriter.

Discs that revolve freely on a fixed axis, or discs that
are fixed to an axle that is free to turn in a gearing, were
used in both ceramics and transportation between 3500

COURTESY OF THE AMERICAN MUSEUM OF NATURAL HISTORY

Votive bronze chariot and bull, probably Syrian

B.C. and 3000 B.C. The earliest evidence of their use comes
from the Fertile Crescent area.

The potter's wheel was a revolutionary invention. The
wheel supplies centrifugal force to a lump of clay thrown into the center. Then when the wheel is moving at a hundred

revolutions a minute or more, the potter presses his hand against the clay and makes it into a circular form. This method of pottery making takes very little effort and produces a far finer receptacle than can be made by coiling or molding. Since potters' wheels are and were usually made of wood, it has been hard for scientists to discover when they were first used, because wood rots, but pots or shards of pots from early Mesopotamia have been found to contain marks indicating that they were made on potters' wheels.

The origin of the wheeled vehicle is even harder to trace, because wheeled vehicles can be made completely of wood and there is no imperishable clay to leave a mark. But in the earliest period of the wheel, vehicles were so valuable they were often buried in royal tombs. Some parts have survived, to show that early wheels were made of three wooden planks carved to fit segments of a circle and clamped together with a pair of transverse wooden struts. The axle was made separately and projected beyond the hub. The hub was made by leaving a swelling in one of the planks, around the axle hole. In some of these vehicles the wheels turned around the axle. In others the axle and the wheels turned together.

The wheel, which made it possible to carry bulky foods from fields to settlements, helped bring about the rise of cities. Farmers could work the open areas, yet live together in large groups for mutual protection.

Before man could even become a farmer, he had to domesticate animals. The dog was the first animal to be domesticated, but a dog did not make a man a farmer. It was the ox and the pig and the sheep, which gave men food and clothing that they did not have to hunt for, that made men farmers. The other side of farming came when men learned to grow crops. Was it science when men sorted out plants and then sowed seeds of wheat and barley in a field? The sorting-out process was the application of brain power and experience to a problem. In the study of various kinds of plants to see which would prosper in the land available, were not these prehistoric men approaching botany?

These are conjectures, since much of what is available to us from the ancient past is in the form of objects. Practically everything that relates to ancient civilizations and societies involves a great deal of guesswork. Scientists of today believe that certain things happened in certain ways. They must adopt some position, if only a trial position, in order to have a basis on which to work out a problem at all. So the history of ancient science is often very fuzzy. Much of what is known is deduced from knowledge about the general civilizations. That is why, in the beginning, the story of science is told along with the history of the growth of the various civilizations. All branches of knowledge have basically the same material with which to work, the material is often sketchy, and even the supposed uses of certain objects are a matter for argument.

Scientists do know that the use and improvement of tools expanded sharply as men began to work the land. Two thousand years before the invention of writing, men in the Fertile Crescent area of the Middle East settled down to farm and to build clay huts. Soon they began to make bricks in a manner that is still used in the Middle East today. The way they made their bricks shows how far in technology men had come at that time.

First the brickmaker prepared a wooden mold, open at the top and bottom. Then he prepared his mixture of soil and water and chopped straw or animal dung which kept the clay from warping or cracking. He selected a flat piece of ground and laid his mold upon it, then dragged a mat which contained the clay mixture alongside. He filled the mold with clay, smoothed off the top with his hand, and when the clay began to dry in the hot sun he removed the mold and left the bricks to bake.

This simple technique required a considerable amount of knowledge. The skilled brickmaker had learned to make a mold. He had learned that even good clay was not enough, but that a tempering material must be used. He had learned not to be misled by outward appearance, but to turn the bricks often even though they seemed dry, to be sure that they were evenly baked. In his technology, by trial and error, he had learned to make generalizations based on many, many experiences.

The brickmaker's work was not science, as we know it, but a beginning of science. The process required thought, experiment, and judgment based on experience. From such humble beginnings developed the tradition that was to lead men to split the atom and send rockets into space.

The traditions and the cultural patterns of civilization made their most rapid strides in the valleys of rivers in northern subtropical areas. The Fertile Crescent, covering much of what are now Iran and Iraq, was one such area. Another was the Nile River Valley of Africa. Others were the Indus and Ganges valleys of India and Persia, and the Yellow and Yangtze valleys of China. The science of Western civilization was to draw much from Egypt, and perhaps the most from the Fertile Crescent,

once that tradition was sparked by a new manner of thinking that arose in Ancient Greece.

By its very physical nature, the area known as the Fertile
Crescent has always been a bridge between the Far Eastern and Mediterranean worlds. It extends in a band
almost from the eastern shore of the Mediterranean to the
Persian Gulf. Today the Tigris and Euphrates rivers join
at the eastern end of the crescent before they reach the
Persian Gulf, but in ancient times the two rivers ran
separate courses to that sea.

The southern portion of the valley extended some
eighty miles between the rivers, and it was on this land
that a civilization grew. Before the invention of writing,
a city had been erected near the Persian Gulf by the
Sumerians, a people who reclaimed the marshes along
the Lower Euphrates. They drained the land and irri-
gated it with canals. They used wheeled vehicles, and
oxen and donkeys to draw them. They cultivated grains
and learned to grow fruits. They built complicated cities
around huge temples called ziggurats. And they invented
a system of writing, the most decisive discovery in the
story of civilization and science.

The Sumerians came to the delta between the Tigris
and Euphrates somewhere between 5000 B.C. and 4000
B.C. By about 3500 B.C. their civilization had grown so
complicated that there was need for a system of written
communication that extended beyond the simple picture.
Men in many places could carve or chisel pictures of animals and plants, but a picture was a poor record of the
affairs of men. Consider how complex was the civilization that developed around Sumer: Each city worshiped
a god of its own. Each god had his temple, and each temple

Babylonian clay tablet listing payments for temple service

had its priests. The common land was held in the ownership of the god, and the priests administered affairs. Men paid their taxes to the god, through the priests, and the priests kept records of the taxes received.

Such early records often consisted of a simple drawing of an item—a cow's head, a unit of grain, a fish. Clay tablets, unearthed at the Sumerian city of Erech, are believed to be records of taxes. They hold signs that are also thought to be numerical—showing how much was paid. Certain tablets are pierced with holes, leading students to believe they represented receipted tax bills.

These earliest records eventually gave way to more complicated tablets. Some showed a man's head and mouth, accompanied by a drawing of food. By 3000 B.C. the Sumerian system of writing included some 500 different signs, which could be used to give such complicated

COURTESY OF THE AMERICAN MUSEUM OF NATURAL HISTORY

Earliest known map, found near Kirkuk in what was ancient Mesopotamia, 2400–2000 B.C.

information as the proper names of kings and deities. As writing improved, the pictographs, or pictures of things, gave way to special signs that called for certain sounds in the spoken language. Although the Sumerians did not develop an alphabet, they did invent a system of writing which let them transmit records that can be read today.

The original pictographs gave way to symbols because of the need for speed in writing down the facts. In the Fertile Crescent, the writing material, or surface, was a clay tablet, and the writing instrument was a stick of reed. As these objects were refined the sticks took on a uniform appearance, and the writing became stylized into wedge-shaped characters called cuneiform. Still it was hard to draw on the clay surface, even with a sharp point. It was easier to make up groups of symbols of different sizes and shapes by using the wedge-shaped reed end to form them. This written language survived the downfall of the original Sumerians, who were conquered by the Akkadians, and it was adopted by nearly all the area, even as the area changed. Cuneiform became the diplomatic language of the Near East and was in use until the beginning of the Christian Era.

Around 2000 B.C. the great conquerer Hammurabi swept through the Tigris Valley and along much of the territory of the Euphrates. He unified this land and extended his own system of laws into the territory he subjugated. Although the system was not new it has become well known as the first written legal code to come down to the modern world. Most of the code was written in cuneiform on a black stone which was discovered by a French archaeological party in Persia in 1902. With this find as a base archaeologists were able to reconstruct the missing parts from other tablets and complete the 282 articles of the code to give a picture of justice and civilization that is nearly four thousand years old.

Hammurabi's laws were divided into six groups. They dealt with movable property, land, business, family relationships, injuries, and labor. These areas of society were by that time so complex that a clear system of laws was essential. It is important to understand that the civilization of four thousand years ago *was* complex, and that no matter how strange their conduct and their worship of gods may seem to modern people, the Babylonians of ancient times were not men with the minds of children, but civilized beings who had made great strides in a knowledge of their world.

For example, consider the problems of building an

urban civilization in an area where it rains very little. Water must be obtained in large quantities. How did the ancients of the Fertile Crescent solve the water problem?

They dug wells, apparently in a manner still followed by the Bedouins of the Arab wastes. First they chose a likely spot, perhaps where some vegetation was growing, then they made a hole with hoes or digging sticks. The packed earth was piled around the hole to form a parapet to keep out animals and to shield the hole from sand. The diggers kept working down until they found water. Next they learned how to line the well to keep the earth from collapsing, and invented a lifting device to bring water up from the well.

In the palace of Ashurnasipal II, who lived at Nimrud, archaeologists found three excellent wells. One was 330 brick courses deep and still held water, nearly three thousand years after it was constructed.

Another manner of getting water was to collect it behind dams as it fell during the spring. A double dam of masonry, built diagonally across the Khosr River above Nineveh, is still standing in part.

An indication of the high development of Babylonian civilization can be found in the system of irrigation of the lands. In the huge river valley between Akkad and Sumer, the temperature ranges between 30 degrees (Fahrenheit) in the winter and 120 degrees in the summer. Some rain falls in that area, but never enough to provide for prosperous growth of crops. The farmers—from the small, stocky Sumerians to their larger Semitic conquerors of later years—all depended on irrigation for successful agriculture.

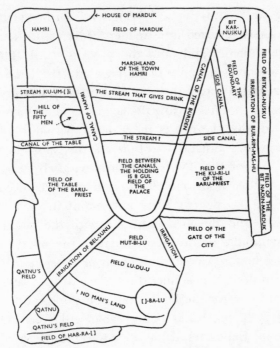

Ancient map of fields and canals in Nippur, Mesopotamia

In the spring, usually in March, the Tigris and the Euphrates often rose suddenly, almost without warning. If both rivers rose at the same time, they were likely to burst their banks and flood the area between. The first line of defense of the farmers was the building of dikes. An early legend of Sumer, which resembles the story of Noah and the great flood in some respects, tells of the fearful flood dragon Kur, who was conquered by the god Ninurta. The victorious god then built a huge dam of stones that controlled the floods and made the land safe for men.

The control of floods did not in itself bring water to the crops, however. Sumerian fields were ridged with temporary walls and ditches. Water was brought through large canals, diverted into smaller feeder canals, and then into the ditches and onto the plots in turn. This system was successful only if the flow into the large canals was regulated carefully and if storage reservoirs were built to catch water during the flood season, to be retained for use during the rest of the growing period.

The greatest canal of that time was the Nahrwan, which flowed out of the Tigris and then paralleled the river. It was 400 feet wide and 200 miles long. It required engineering knowledge to build and maintain such a large waterway, and the men entrusted with the task had to understand the nature of their river, the nature of the soil, and how to calculate in terms of water flow. Canals must run down an incline; the surface of the water must be slightly above the land level; the slope must not be too steep, or the banks of the canal will erode. On the Tigris and Euphrates, if the slope were not steep enough, weeds and silt would choke the channels. The engineers who supervised this work needed to know how much work a man could do, how many men would be required to dig or maintain a certain portion of a canal, and how long a specific job would take. Babylonian civilization, then, required a sophisticated system of mathematics.

Babylonian mathematics was quite equal to such tasks. Sumerian numeration was, in the beginning, a mixture of decimal and sexagesimal ideas. It would be difficult for anyone but a trained mathematician to understand some of the ways in which they made their calculations (based on the figure 60), but they were extremely accurate.

The Babylonians also understood geometrical principles, although they solved geometrical problems with algebra when possible. They used their mathematics in problems that dealt with agriculture and engineering, with measurements of weights and values of precious goods, in military matters, and in astronomy. Mathematics in Babylon was excellent, although little of it was transmitted to the Western world. For a time the Greeks drew on this older knowledge, but later they dropped it. Still later, a Babylonian concept of placement or position in numeration was picked up through the Moslem world in what has come to be known as the system of Arabic numerals.

Other Babylonian concepts—such as negative numbers —were unknown to the West until the sixteenth century. The Babylonian idea of using the same base for numbers and the science of weights and measures did not become familiar to the West until the development of the metric system in the late eighteenth century. But to this day we still divide the circle into 360 degrees, and the degree by 60, using the sexagesimal system invented in Ancient Babylon.

The astronomy of the Fertile Crescent area falls into three separate classifications. First was the astronomy of the Sumerians, Akkadians, and other very ancient peoples —perhaps the most ancient scientific astronomy in history. The second period was that of the Assyrians, in about the seventh century B.C., and the third era is that of the Chaldeans, from whom the Greeks drew a great deal of their information and scientific practice. The Chaldean period—or what is generally called Chaldean—extended to within two hundred years of the Christian Era.

The confusions, for the most part, lie outside the Fertile Crescent area and relate to the effects of the science of the area on others. Within the Fertile Crescent, the works of the most ancient Babylonians were handed down to later ones. In astronomy particularly, the chain of observations was nearly continuous, and astronomical observation was a contribution of the old Babylonians. The ancient Sumerians observed the heavens from the tops of their ziggurats. They created a calendar based on a year of 360 days divided into twelve months. When necessary they inserted a thirteenth month to make the calendar come out right. They also introduced the idea of equality of the divisions of the day into hours, rather than subdividing the ever-changing periods of daylight and darkness. The Sumerians began their day at sunset because the moon god Sin was a most important deity. Until Hammurabi, most of the city-states had their own calendars, but he unified the calendar for the whole region.

Babylonian astronomers are noted particularly for their observations of the planet Venus, and while Babylonian astrology drew heavily on readings of animal and human organs—especially the liver—the stars played a part in magic and astrology, too. But astrology—the determination of human events based on observation and magical speculation—did not blind the astronomers. Observations were carried out faithfully and accurately. The astrological interpretations were quite another matter. Thus ancient Babylonian observers knew the relative positions of the planets, the sun, and the moon and the stars they saw above them, and they left written records that would be of great importance to later students of astronomy. The Assyrians preserved and codified much of this knowledge. The Chaldeans brought it much further and made astronomy a mathematical science that included a systematic theory to govern eclipses.

The Babylonian sky was a boat, an overturned *gufa* (the round woven reed boat still used on the rivers of the area), and their earth was an image of the heavens, a small place bounded by the four countries known to the early Sumerians. But that was cosmology, which was mixed up with the gods. When it came to geography of their own region, the ancients were quite at home. One mapmaker drew a plan of the ancient city of Nippur—one so accurate that archaelogists were able to follow it faithfully in excavating the city. With geography as well as with astronomy, mathematics was involved. The contribution of mathematics overshadowed all others of the Babylonians to science, and it was this mathematical concept which was to prove so useful to the later Hellenes.

The people of the Fertile Crescent left records of large numbers of animals and plants that they knew well. Two thousand years before our era, a Babylonian king left notes dealing with thirty different types of fish sold on the market. Two hundred and fifty different plants were described in other clay tablets. The ancients of the area divided animals into those which live in the water, "those which are segmented," serpents, birds, and four-legged animals. Plants were divided into trees, edibles, spices, drugs, cereals, and fruits. The Babylonians raised date palms and prized the fruit. They learned that nonbearing palms—male date palms—must be brought in contact with fruit-bearing female palms if they are to produce dates. Perhaps they did not understand the theory of plant fertilization, which was not postulated until the late seventeenth century of the Christian Era, but nearly four thousand years earlier they did know how to raise date palms.

The same competence that made the people of Babylon

COURTESY OF THE AMERICAN MUSEUM OF NATURAL HISTORY

A gufa, a round woven reed boat of the type used by Babylonians

good farmers extended to other occupations. They built large, planned cities centered around their temples. Usually these temples were built of mud brick, but after 3000 B.C. the brick was baked in a kiln rather than dried in the sun. Stone and cement bricks also were used. They built pavements and platforms, and decorated their public buildings with statues and friezes.

One temple excavated at El-Ubaid shows how intricate was their work, even in those relatively early times. It stood on a brick platform high above the street level, and was approached by a broad flight of stone steps flanked by brick walls. The steps led to an open portico with wooden columns overlaid with copper or with a mosaic made of mother-of-pearl, black shale, and red limestone set in bitumen. The entrance to the temple was guarded by life-sized copper lion heads whose inlaid eyes and teeth gave them a lifelike appearance.

Inside, the walls were covered with copper figures of bulls and friezes of other figures inlaid in colors against black shale.

These temple builders invented the arch and such niceties as plumbing. In one temple at Eshnunna, bathrooms with toilets were built along the outer side of the building, so that their drains discharged into a closed sewer that ran the length of the street. The sewers could be opened for inspection and cleaning. The bathrooms were paved, and the toilets were fitted with seats.

The large buildings measured about 150 by 250 feet in length and breadth, and stood 75 feet high, but these builders also erected palaces and less ornate homes for business and professional men.

The Babylonians were great traders; their geographical position between the Mediterranean and the Far East assured them new ideas, new materials, and new goods. They worked in copper, bronze, silver, and tin. In 2250 B.C., an artisan made a bronze portrait head of King Sargon—a work of art that could scarcely be called primitive. Craftsmen cast huge doors of bronze and hammered intricate reliefs into copper and gold utensils, soldering and welding metals together.

These highly civilized men built bridges, including one which crossed the Euphrates to join the two sections of the old city of Babylon. The river was a thousand yards wide at that point, and the builders erected more than

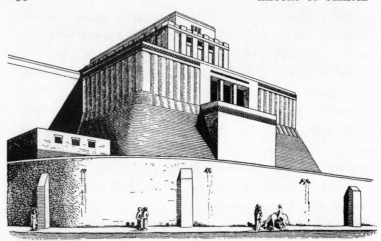

Reconstruction of a temple at Eridu, in Mesopotamia in the fourth millennium

a hundred stone piers to support the bridge. Across that bridge ran wheeled vehicles, carts, war chariots, and wagons.

As their region prospered the Babylonians developed many industries. They made pottery and glazed it. They manufactured paints, dyes, drugs, soaps and cosmetics. They made glass. They were perfumers and brewers. In this respect, although they did not conceive of chemistry as a science, they practiced chemical manufacturing.

Babylonian medicine was closely related to magic and the worship of their gods. The first physicians were priests. Some doctors were entrusted with the interpretation of magical signs and omens that would tell them the nature and course of a disease. Some were exorcists who used magic to drive out the evil spirits that caused the patient to be sick. Others were physicians, as we know them, who treated patients and gave them drugs.

The civilization of Babylon was harsh in its very nature; it adhered to the philosophy of "An eye for an eye and a tooth for a tooth." Hammurabi's code, for example, specified that a physician who treated a nobleman for a wound and cured him was to be given ten shekels of silver (about 130 grains). But if that nobleman died, the physician's hands were to be cut off. For the same medical treatment given a commoner, the reward was only five shekels, and the punishment for failure was less severe. For a slave the reward was only two shekels, but if the slave died, the physician had only to replace him at his own expense.

The practice of veterinary medicine was less hazardous to the practitioner's life and limb. A veterinarian who performed a successful operation on an ox received only one-sixth of a shekel for his work, but if the animal died, he was forced to pay the owner one-fourth of its value.

In a case of serious human illness, it was the custom for the doctor to examine the entrails of a sacrificed animal to determine the cause of the patient's illness and his chances of survival. The liver was considered the most important organ of the body, and there are many references to it in Babylonian tablets. Models of the liver were carefully drawn, and the surfaces were divided into many areas. If the liver of a sheep showed certain abnormalties in one area, the doctor-priest paid particular attention to the omens attached to that area and based his diagnosis on his discoveries.

There was no conscious trickery in the belief that human ills could be diagnosed by examining the entrails of animals. Physicians and their patients believed that the gods thus showed their pleasure or displeasure, and the gods ruled the lives of men. Although this manner of diagnosis may not have given the Babylonian doctors much knowledge of human anatomy, it led to close observation of a limited area. Eventually the study of anatomy was to be the result.

Historian George Sarton compares Babylonian medicine in some respects to the present-day practice of Christian Science. For instance, in about 1750 B.C., King Tabiutul-Enlil was stricken with a frightful disease. A tablet dating from that period described it in the king's own words. He was bedridden, paralyzed, blind and deaf, and his food tasted bitter; his joints ached and his entire body was tortured with pain. The king reported that the disease of his joints baffled his chief exorciser. The diviner could discover no clear omens about the king's future. He could not tell the limit of the illness, and the exorciser could not tell the character of the illness. But in a dream the god Enlil came to the king and drove away the disease, even as the king's subjects were preparing his grave. The god opened the king's eyes and ears. The king had not been able to speak; suddenly he could. His tongue had been swollen, but the swelling disappeared. He was cured of scurvy and the itch. The cure came not from the medical men but from the god, said the king. The old king had clung to his faith and was sure it had saved him.

Besides the liver, physicians used many other means of divining the nature of illness. They poured oil on water and read in the shapes of the spreading oil the signs of the future. They watched the flight of birds and questioned the patient about his dreams. They set considerable store in the omens of the stars, but this came later than the great empires of the Sumerians, Akkadians, and Babylonians.

Once the physician-priest had determined the nature of the illness of a patient, the gods were asked to heal the illness. Evil spirits could be driven out by incantations, and the priests sometimes named one evil spirit after another, in a hit-and-miss fashion, hoping that the responsible demon would be among them. Certain demons controlled certain illnesses—the pain of toothache was supposed to come from the gnawing of a worm.

But the Babylonians did not content themselves with magic. They used tubes to blow remedies into the eyes and nose and ears, and ointments and poultices for skin ailments. The priest-doctors knew some 250 plants and 120 mineral substances to which they attributed medical properties. Some of the remedies were foul and evil-tasting and many of them were employed to make the demon sick and to force him to leave the body. Others, such as sulphur, proved physically effective with skin diseases.

Scholars are in some disagreement as to the time during which Babylonian culture became the dominant force in the civilized world. Not far away from Babylonia, Egypt developed a culture of its own during a roughly similar period. Here, in speaking of events of five, four, and three thousand years ago, much is known but much is unknown. It is safe to say that there were two great Middle Eastern cultures, that they acted on one another in days long before the birth of Christ, and both provided aspects of the heritage of Greek civilization. The interplay between the civilizations of Babylon and those of the areas farther east is not fully known. For many years, particularly in the nineteenth century in the Western world, it was believed that Chinese civilization was very, very old. But history, apart from legend, begins in China less than two thousand years before the birth of Christ. The civilization of the Indus Valley flourished at least around 2000 B.C.—the time of Hammurabi of the Babylonia area—and *after* the great pyramid age of Egypt. If one were to try to choose a single period in which all these civilizations existed, it would probably be best to select a point in history around 1500 B.C. when Babylon could be said to be on the wane, when Egypt was strong, and when Far Eastern societies are traceable by history, not by legend.

CHAPTER **2**

Science in the Far East

ONE cannot actually compare the development of sciences and scientific thought in the Babylonian, Egyptian, and Far Eastern worlds, because they occurred at different times and followed individual patterns. Nor is there any purpose to such comparisons at an early period in the tracing of the history of the science of the Western world.

Comparisons between the scientific backgrounds of the Far East and the Near East are valuable, however, if they give some insight into reasons for the differences in development of Western and Eastern civilizations. Such comparisons ought also to lay at rest tales from two extremes: that Far Eastern science was much older and far more developed than Western science, or that Far Eastern science did not exist independently.

A pre-Aryan civilization in the Indus Valley sprang up very early in the history of mankind. Scholars do not yet know much about that civilization, but excavations have shown that three thousand years before the Christian Era, peoples in the Punjab and Sind areas lived in planned cities. They had developed pictographic writing. They had standards of art and craftsmanship that did not suffer overly in comparison with those of the Fertile Crescent region. They used burned bricks in building, they built systems of street drainage, they developed a system of weights and measures, and they worked in copper and bronze.

Around 1500 B.C., this society was overrun by Aryan tribes which entered India from the northwest and occupied the river valleys of the Indus and the Ganges. These Aryans built an advanced civilization, but except for some fragments and generalizations, the details have not been unraveled. A major problem in this respect has been the absence of a reliable chronology of Ancient India. Another is the unwillingness of Indian and Ceylonese practitioners to seek integration with Western ideas. Joseph Needham, engaged in a vast scholarly work on ancient Chinese science and medicine, has found that southern Asians are much less interested than the Chinese in finding common ground with the West in such matters as medicine and the use of drugs.

What is known is that science was not neglected in that civilization. A solar eclipse was mentioned in the Rig-Veda, an important historical, legendary and literary book of India. Arithmetic and higher forms of mathematics were used, and this society and Chinese societies exchanged material in the second millennium, or before 1000 B.C. Students of technology have discovered the existence of madder dye in the Indus civilization prior to 2500 B.C. and the arrival of the Aryans. This dye was found in fragments of cloth unearthed in diggings. So a practical chemistry was known.

One major achievement was the formulation of an advanced written language—Sanskrit—before Alexander the Great conquered Persia and brought a Hellenic influence to Indian civilization in the fourth century B.C.

Nearly five thousand years ago, these people developed wheeled vehicles that remained basically unchanged—with the exception of additions of the spoke—until the twentieth century. Before the Hellenic period, outstanding successes in medicine and surgery were enjoyed in parts of India, and in the age of the Buddha—a century before the Alexandrian period began—India boasted two great universities. It might be expected that when the Greeks rubbed against the Indian civilization, the two would contribute greatly to one another. There was interchange, three hundred years before the beginning of the Christian Era, but it was far from complete. It is suggested that one reason for this lack of unity was a basic philosophical difference between East and West. Certainly after Buddhism became an important factor in the Far East the very introversion of this religion led Easterners to look homeward rather than abroad.

If there is much confusion in the West regarding the course of scientific history in southern Asia, until recent years there was far more Western confusion regarding the development of Chinese civilization. Only within the last few years has an authoritative Western study of Chinese science and civilization been attempted in a comprehensive work by Joseph Needham, with a number of scholarly associates, at Cambridge University. A century earlier, historians confused fact, fancy, and legend to show a general picture of a highly developed Chinese civilization that extended five thousand years and more in the past. Needham has established a beginning point for a true historical tradition shortly after 1500 B.C., which means that in comparison to the civilizations of the Middle East, the Nile, and the Indus, the Chinese civilization was young. Needham's point of beginning was found in some oracle bones on which Chinese writing could be deciphered—bones that date back to the fourteenth century B.C.—and on which the written characters can be linked with the Chinese language of the twentieth century. The problem for history students, then, is not to wonder why the fruits of ancient Chinese civilization did

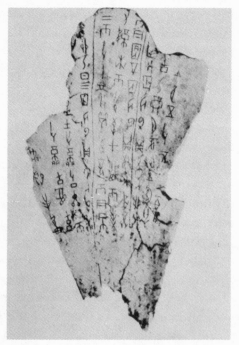

Chinese oracle bone, showing inscriptions

not travel to the Euphrates and the Nile, but to determine what influence Egypt, Babylon, and the Indus civilization had on China. With China more than with India, there has been overemphasis on mystery and legend. For many years China's civilization was given credit it did not deserve. At the same time, through other misunderstanding, Chinese civilization was denied certain valid credit. For example, it is known now that long before any Western group accepted the idea of an infinite universe, China's students of the heavens held just such a theory.

The Shang period, during which the oracle bones were buried, is the first that modern historians accept as truly historic in China. But again, the physical evidence comes from a time when a civilization was already well formed. In the Shang period, Needham says, the Chinese system of numerals was more advanced and more scientific than either those of Ancient Babylon or of Ancient Egypt. Earlier, in the Hsia period—2205 to 1766 B.C.—Chinese civilization is credited by legend with having developed irrigation, agriculture, writing, calendars, and the arts of pottery making and metal work. Still, the Shang numeral system was truly remarkable. Needham notes that on the old oracle bones the figures for 547 days were written, in Chinese characters, in this manner: five hundreds, four tens, and seven days. And while a thousand years later the Ancient Romans wrote the figure 300 as CCC, these Chinese could show the same quantity with two characters—one signifying three, the other the hundred unit. Nor could there be confusion, because the Chinese symbol for *hundred* could not stand by itself as the Roman *C* did. The Chinese symbol had to be defined by a figure. The Chinese of the Shang period were able to express any number, however large, without using more than nine numerals. Here, then, Needham believes, was the origin of the "Arabic" numerals that were to cross the Himalayas to India, thence to the thriving Arabic world of the period known to the West as the Dark Ages, and finally to an awakening western Europe.

The oldest Chinese culture seems to have emerged in the region along the Yellow River that springs from mountains in the heart of Asia and traces a tortuous course to the Yellow Sea. From that time onward, the development of Chinese technology and Chinese science was continual, without more than peripheral influences from the West. In other words, China developed its own scientific tradition quite apart from the remainder of the world, except for the Indians—their closest neighbors. For practical purposes, until the development of modern science, Japan was a part of the Chinese scientific community. China's rulers and scholars came under serious Western influence in the seventeenth century of the Christian Era when Jesuit missionaries traveled to the Orient to convert the heathen and study their ways. In the span between the Shang period and the Christian seventeenth century, Chinese science developed in quite a different manner than Western science. The Chinese system of astronomy was as logical as Western astronomy but Chinese astronomy was based on circumpolar stars while Western astronomy was based on ecliptic measurements, or the great circular path that the earth courses about the sun.

In the field of mathematics, the ancient Chinese were extremely active. In 1936, a pair of Chinese scholars published a catalogue of the mathematical books in the libraries of Peking, which totaled more than a thousand titles

—most of them written before the period of intensive European influence in the Christian seventeenth century.

One very old scientific work is the *Chou Pei Suan Ching*. At one time, students of Chinese history believed that it represented mathematics in China of the year 1100 B.C., but that dating has been advanced to a point far nearer the beginning of the Christian Era. Part of the work consists of a dialogue between the Duke of Chou and a man of some importance called Shang Kao on the properties of the right-angle triangle. In it the principle of the Pythagorean theorem is stated (the square of the hypotenuse of a right-angled triangle equals the sum of the squares of the other two sides). It is not proved in the Euclidian manner, but it is stated.

Another section of this book refers to the use of the gnomon (a rod to measure the shadow of the sun), the circle and the square. The book mentions measurements of heights and distances. It also discusses matters of interest to mathematicians and astronomers: measurement of the sun's diameter by use of a sighting tube; calculations of the annual movement of the sun; descriptions of methods for determining the meridian by observations; and lists of sun-shadow lengths for each of the fortnightly periods of the year the Chinese observed.

Another early Chinese book was the *Chiu Chang Suan Shu,* which contained nine chapters with 246 problems, probably the most important of all Chinese mathematical books. It gives mathematical rules for surveying land and for determining percentages and proportions of grains. In the section on engineering, the book deals with questions about city walls, dikes, canals, and rivers. Another portion concerns problems of taxation.

About two hundred years after the birth of Christ, in the period known as San Kuo (Three Kingdoms), a number of other Chinese works were prepared. Scholars are not certain as to dates, but these books show a wide range of knowledge in technical and scientific fields. One discusses weights and measures and the densities of various metals. A handbook for government officials was prepared to teach them the measurement of areas. In this period when Europe lived in the Dark Ages Chinese and Indian mathematics were far superior to those of the West.

Chinese printing began in the eighth century, nearly seven hundred years before printing was established in the Western world, and the Chinese classics were then printed and far more widely distributed than before. In the days of Kubla Khan, a famous mathematician named Kuo Shou-ching carried out the building of dams and canals and worked in the fields of astronomy and calendar preparation. At this time the influence of the Arabic world was felt in China for the Khans ranged wide in their conquests and rubbed shoulders with the Arabs of the eastern Moslem Empire.

From very early times, the Chinese used bones and counting rods in their arithmetical calculations. Shortly after the beginning of the Christian Era, they developed the abacus, a counting machine with which experts could work as quickly as modern Americans can work an electric calculating machine. (In 1946, a competition was staged in Tokyo between a Japanese clerk using an abacus and an American soldier using a calculating machine. The abacus won all contests except those involving multiplication.)

Before 1000 B.C., Chinese mathematicians were familiar

Chinese abacus

with algebraic problems. It has been suggested that while the Chinese algebra was not the algebra students know today, it may have contributed to Arabic algebra, which was carried to the West toward the end of the Middle Ages.

Throughout the early history of China, the major importance of mathematics was its service in working with calendar computations. From very early days, one sign of the power of the ruling king was his right to issue the calendar for use by the people, which he did through his dukes and lesser nobles. Chinese mathematicians did not trouble themselves, by and large, with abstract ideas—as did the Greeks. Chinese philosophy, leaning on the ideas of the Buddha, the Confucianists, and the Taoists, held that the universe was a self-sufficient organic system, without a supreme God or creator, and that all the universe lived in order, not governed by what we know as laws of nature. The Chinese, then, sought no abstract explanations—and this is a basic difference between the development of the sciences, particularly the mathemati-

cal sciences, in East and West. Nor was there any mixing
between the gentlemen of the Chinese courts, who practiced the higher arts of mathematics, surveyed the heavens,
and corrected the calendar when necessary, with the humble artisans who built houses and boats and worked with
metals.

Chinese astronomers, from the beginning of history,
were persons of considerable importance and nearly all
of them were nobles of the courts of the emperors. Perhaps the Chinese derived their original scientific impetus
from the astronomers of the Fertile Crescent—this idea
has been advanced, but scholars have not agreed on a
beginning. The *Shu Ching*, the great classic Chinese history of ancient times, tells how the Emperor Yao sent
the brothers Hsi and Ho to work to study the sun, the
moon, the stars, and the markers of the seasons. He sent
Hsi to live among the barbarians at a place named Yang-
ku, "and to receive as a guest the rising sun, in order to
regulate the labors of the east."

Hsi also went to Nan-Chiao to study the summer solstice, while Ho was sent to live in the west and "bid fare-
well respectfully to the setting sun, in order to regulate
the western or autumnal accomplishment." He further
ordered the youngest brother Ho to live in the north in
order to supervise the works of the north.

Now this is legend, not history. In recent years historians have shown that Hsi-Ho is the name given the
mythological being which is sometimes the chariot driver
to the sun. In legend, the emperor then sent four men
to the ends of the earth, to stop the sun and turn it back
on its course at the solstices, and to send it on its way at
the equinoxes. These magicians also were ordered to

prevent eclipses, and when two of them failed, the emperor sent a punitive expedition after them to destroy them.

The importance of this legend is that it shows how highly the ancients in China regarded the matter of astronomy as a part of the state religion. Early in history, the astronomical observatory appeared in the emperor's palace, and the astronomers were a part of the palace retinue. In western Szechuan Province and elsewhere, remains of old irrigation systems still exist, and have been honored by the Chinese for many hundreds of years as symbols of the culture of their land. It took an accurate calendar to keep the people living on the land happy, for it was the emperor's self-chosen duty to prevent the seasons from surprising his people.

A manuscript of about 200 B.C. describes the responsibilities of the Imperial Astronomer. He concerned himself with the twelve-year periods that were based on the revolution of Jupiter, and with the hours of the day and the days of the ten-day week. He observed the sun and checked it carefully at the summer and winter solstices and the moon at the spring and fall equinoxes, to determine the coming of the four seasons.

Another important official was the Imperial Astrologer, who observed the planets, the sun, the moon, and the stars, for a different reason. It was his responsibility to tell of the coming of good and bad fortune to the kingdom. He divided the kingdom and its tributary states into nine regions, and related each region to different heavenly bodies. Thus, through the stars he could predict the coming of good and bad times. He watched the cycle of Jupiter, too, to predict good and evil. He examined the heavenly clouds, dividing them into five different kinds; from the color of clouds he determined the coming of floods, drought, famine, or good harvests. He noted twelve different kinds of winds that had direct bearing on the well-being of the empire.

These high offices of astronomer and astrologer continued through Chinese history even to the Manchu dynasty of the nineteenth century—although by the nineteenth century the purely hereditary offices had little actual function and the astrologer and astronomer were in no sense scientists.

Lesser observatories existed within the dukedoms and at the universities, but the practice of astronomy and astrology were carefully guarded by the imperial house,

A Chinese planisphere for showing the position of the stars

and the security regulations governing their activities were severe. In 840 A.D., an imperial edict forbade astronomical officials and their staffs to mix with ordinary civil servants and the common people. The degree of secrecy, however, depended largely on the emperor in power, and at times the study of astronomy was encouraged among the nobility and in the universities.

The earliest known Chinese calendar was a farmer's calendar issued sometime around the fifth century before Christ. It followed the twelve lunar months of the year. Another calendar issued slightly later—the Yuëh Ling—was far more detailed. It provided certain astronomical data and much discussion of ceremonies and sacrifices to be performed in the various periods. In calendar making and in astronomy the Chinese did take material from the Babylonians—material that came to them through India and later through traffic with Westerners across Turkestan and along similar caravan routes. In the beginning, of course, the term Westerner was relative—it meant someone farther west than the Chinese, and this included the Middle Eastern peoples.

The Chinese accepted several theories that related to the composition of the universe. In one, called the Kai Thien theory, the heavens were held to be a semicircular cover, over an earth that was a bowl upside down—but it was a square earth. Another theory, known as Hun Thien, held that the heavens were like a hen's egg, and the earth like the yolk of the egg, lying alone in the center. A third theory held that the sun, moon and stars floated freely in empty space. This theory was called the Hsüan Thien theory. It predated by more than a thousand years the discovery by Europeans that the heavens did not move about in crystallized spheres. Of course not all these theories were held at one time by Chinese cosmologists. They prospered at different times between the dawn of Chinese history and the coming of the Jesuits to China.

Part of the test of any collection of astronomical information by a society is the mapping of stars. The Chinese carried out extensive mapping programs, and accurate observations of the heavens, beginning at least four centuries before the birth of Christ. From the fifth to tenth centuries of the Christian Era, China's observations stand nearly alone today for the reference of astronomers who wish to seek accurate information about the state of the heavens in that period. Arabic astronomy had not yet flourished, the Hellenic tradition had all but disappeared, and the West had gone into its deep sleep.

By the middle of the second century, the Chinese had mapped at least 118 constellations which contained 780 stars, and one astronomer of the period wrote that he knew of the existence of some 14,000 stars. Because they followed a different tradition, the Chinese named their stars and constellations in a manner quite different from those of Middle Easterners and Westerners. But they used some of the same tools, such as planispheres cast in bronze or painted on paper and silk.

The gnomon, a simple vertical pole used to cast a shadow, was the oldest of Chinese astronomical instruments. With it, the Duke of Lu measured the winter solstice in the year 654 B.C., according to Chinese legend. If, as is probable, he actually only supervised the measurement, nonetheless the instrument was in use. Many centuries later, the gnomon was increased to a tremendous size. At the end of the thirteenth century, the famous astronomer Kuo Shou-ching built a huge structure for the purpose of measuring shadows. Known as Chou Kung's tower, it was situated about five miles southeast of the modern city of Loyang. It was essentially a pyramid, with a slot in the center. The sides were 50 feet wide at

Tower of Chou Kung

the bottom and 25 feet wide at the top, which was reached by two sets of stairs. On the north side of the building was a room with a wide opening and a view of the top of a separate gnomon 40 feet in height which cast a shadow on the ground. The shadow ran along a 120-foot measuring scale. Here officials of the empire gathered to measure the solstices and to prepare their reports for the emperor.

Ancient Chinese astronomers also made use of the

sundial for telling time in the daylight hours. As in the Western world the Chinese produced portable as well as fixed sundials.

The clepsydra, or water clock, is sometimes credited to China, but the fact is that it was invented, long before the beginning of Chinese history, by the Babylonians and Egyptians. The Chinese had many types of water clocks, including one variety in which the water was used to turn a wheel that rotated an indicator.

A type of clepsydra, or water clock, in the Imperial Palace, Peking

Chang Ĥeng, a famous astronomer, wrote about another kind of water clock. It was made of bronze vessels placed one above the other and filled with water. Water dripping from the top vessel made its way down to the others. On the cover of the last receiver was a small bronze statuette. The change in water level caused the statuette to guide an indicator rod with its left hand, and indicate the graduations on it with its right hand, thus telling the time.

Chinese incense clocks

The Chinese divided the day into twelve equal "double hours" and into a hundred "quarters," for more accurate measurement. They used the sundial, the clepsydra, and mechanical clocks that they invented in about the eleventh century B.C. They also used a remarkable method of telling time that has not persisted, but which seems to have been controllable in its accuracy—the incense clock.

Father Gabriel Magalhaens, one of the Jesuit priests who came to China in the seventeenth century, wrote in wonder about the incense clocks. He described how the Chinese first beat a certain incense wood into powder, then rolled it into ropes or cast it in a mold to assure uniform thickness. They then constructed a cone of incense rope, placing marks on the cone to show the time that had elapsed as the cone burned slowly down in the manner of a firecracker fuse.

These clocks were used widely by businessmen, travelers, and scholars. They even had an alarm device. The clock user would hang a small weight at the point that represented the hour when he wanted to arise. When the burning of the incense reached that mark, the material supporting the weight would be burned through, allowing the weight to fall into a brass bowl placed below. The resulting noise would awaken the sleeper. Father Magalhaens found the Chinese clocks wonderful, partly because they were so inexpensive that nearly everyone could afford to use them.

Chinese astronomers also used a sighting tube shaped like a modern telescope tube, though without lenses. It was valuable in limiting the view of the sky, thus giving the observer an opportunity to concentrate his vision.

In the eleventh century, Su Sung, a Chinese astronomer, built a huge device called an astronomical clock tower. It stood 40 feet high. Concealed within the structure was a giant water wheel fed by a huge reservoir. Each night men came to pump water from the bottom of the structure into the upper reservoir. Each day the water dripped steadily in a controlled flow, filling buckets on the wheel, one after the other. Every quarter of an hour the wheel, its buckets loaded, tripped an escape mechanism that moved the entire tower. This movement was regulated so

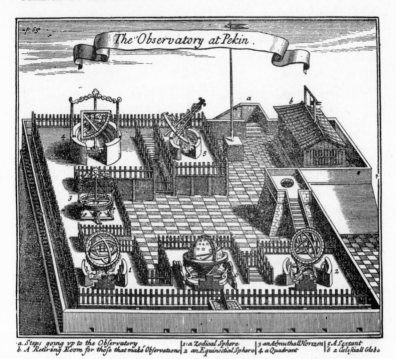

Woodcut of the observatory at Peking, reproduced from Le Comte's Voyage to China, *1698*

that observing instruments on the top of the tower turned automatically to follow the apparently moving heavens. In a room below, a marked globe also rotated at the same rate, showing the astronomer the risings and settings of the stars and planets.

On the front of the tower was a small pagoda with a series of doors, one atop the other. At appointed hours, when the escapement of the clock tower acted, the doors opened and small figures came out on mechanical pedestals. These figures held tablets marked with the hours of the day and night, and the whole show was accompanied by ringing bells, clashing cymbals and the banging of Chinese gongs.

Su Sung's tower was well known both in antiquity and to moderns because he wrote widely in a period after printing had begun and because his works were saved although generally they went unread. But not until Derek J. de Solla Price studied it in the twentieth century was Su Sung's tower appreciated for its potential importance to history. Price was interested in clocks; he had found a void in history in the development of the escapement mechanism that makes clockwork possible. With the aid of Joseph Needham and assistants, Price apparently unraveled part of the story of clocks. They discovered that the forerunner of Su Sung's mechanism had been built by the old astronomer Chang Ĥeng sometime shortly after 100 A.D. Further, they came upon indications that not one but three Chinese inventions *might* have been transmitted to Europe—or, rather, two inventions and one delusion. The clock was one. The magnetic compass, which appeared suddenly in Europe at about the same time, was another. Third, the belief of Europeans in perpetual-motion machines—which still exists there and in America—may have come from some European traveler who had seen Su Sung's clockwork tower, without realizing that at night the reservoir of the tower was filled by the heavy labor of a gang of coolies. Price, chairman of the Department of the History of Science at Yale University, suggests that all three ideas came from a traveler who visited Su Sung in China.

The Chinese used the armillary sphere that astronomers found valuable in giving them views of the relative positions and angles of the heavenly bodies without the need of constant astronomical calculation. The armillary sphere was an essential part of Su Sung's tower, and it was to keep the sphere in motion relative to the heavens that the clockwork mechanism was built.

The Chinese were far ahead of the West in some ways, including the adaptation of the armillary sphere to equatorial mountings, which made it effective, and predated by centuries the West's discovery of this system. (It is used today in our huge telescopes such as that at Mount Wilson.)

Because their form of astronomy was not fundamentally mathematical, the Chinese did not trouble themselves as much with the theories of planetary motion as did the Westerners, but some Chinese astronomers seemed to be aware that the planets moved in orbits. In the collected works of Chu Hsi, referring to a period about in the twelfth century, Chinese students refer to "orbits."

Chinese records, while still subject to study and interpretation, have already been found to be valuable to astronomers, in some cases to confirm Western findings, and in others to show that discoveries were made in the Orient before they were in the West—although there was so little contact between the two worlds until the seventeenth century that these discoveries were unknown to Europe. Such matters as sunspots—which Europeans ignored because of their belief of the perfection of the universe—were studied by the Chinese a thousand years before they were studied or recognized in the West by Galileo and his competitors.

Ancient Chinese astronomy, then, was a science—an

important one, both in its own day and in its contribution to the development of all science and culture, East
and West.

And what of other sciences?

Records show that as long ago as the thirteenth century
B.C., Chinese officials kept systematic meteorological records, and that 2,500 years later there were some twenty-
three books on forecasting in Chinese. They used rain
and snow gauges to learn the effects that might be felt
from spring floods. They studied rainbows and the winds.
One imperial officer, whose status was as high as that of
the royal astronomer, primarily was concerned with the
weather. He was charged with the responsibility of explain-
ing it to the people of the empire and of prognosticating
good or bad fortune from the signs he observed.

The records were kept carefully. How they were used
is quite another matter, but if facts were used as the basis
for romantic fancies, it still does not obscure or lessen
their value.

The Chinese were serious students of the tides long
before Europeans, including Galileo, took much note of
them, and by the first century of the Christian Era,
Chinese scientists were aware of the dependence of the
tides on the moon.

Chinese students produced anthropological geographies
early in their nation's recorded history. Until the Dark
Ages, European geographical concepts were ahead of
those of the Orient, but after the decline of interest in
Herodotus and Strabo in the West, China forged ahead.
The Chinese produced geographical encyclopedias in the
third and fourth centuries and improved them steadily
for several hundred years, then lost interest as the people

of Europe regained their own. Chinese explorers journeyed into Afghanistan and Tibet and to other areas, particularly in Central Asia. By the middle of the fourteenth century—before Europe had become fully aware of China—an old map from the Orient showed Europe in nearly true perspective, with 100 place names given, and another 35 place names for Africa. European knowledge of the Orient at that time could in no sense match this Chinese geographical sophistication.

Chinese sailors knew the Persian Gulf, the Red Sea, Aden, the Caspian, the Baltic, and the Black Sea (some of this through the Arabs who settled in Canton before the middle of the eighth century).

Even in the last half of the twentieth century very little study by Westerners has been devoted to other Chinese sciences such as geology and mineralogy. In the sense that they knew dyes and glazes and were quite expert in their use, the Chinese also were chemists. They worked with gunpowder long before it came to the West. They built the forerunner of all seismographs before the end of the second century, when Rome was falling and Greece was dormant.

The Chinese made a pure rag paper long before the West did. They studied botany—the earliest description of the banana was written at the end of the second century. They were alchemists, toying with magic and materials, but from their alchemy came red and black inks.

Medically speaking, the Chinese advanced far and fast. Chang Chung-ching wrote treatises on dietetics and fevers at the end of the second century. Hua T'ao, a surgeon, used wine as a general anesthetic in the third century. Ch'ao Yüan-fang wrote treatises on several diseases, including the eye, genito-urinary problems, and impetigo. The Emperor Kao Tsung of the T'ang dynasty in the last half of the seventh century ordered revision of the empire's medical books into fifty-two volumes.

Other Chinese doctors wrote about female disorders, and the theory of the pulse system is supposedly of Chinese origin. Hu Ssu-hui treated two forms of beriberi; Hua Shou wrote a treatise on the blood vessels in 1341; Chu Tan-ch'i discussed the use of chalmoogra oil as a treatment for leprosy. In the eleventh century, the Chinese were practicing inoculation for smallpox.

Not all of these medical ideas were totally native to China. Some of them came through India, and some, practiced after 200 A.D., reflected other foreign influences.

Prior to that time and the interchange of religion and attitudes that came with Buddhism's move from the south, China had taken large strides in the matter of hygiene and preventive medicine.

The Taoists believed in the possibility of attaining material immortality so that they could exist as real, if ghostly, beings here on earth; they studied alchemy, looked for drugs which would give long life or immortality, and did all they could to save both body and soul from trouble.

For many years foreigners have laughed in misunderstanding of an old Chinese way of thinking. Hearing that the Chinese people "paid the doctor when they were well, and he treated them without pay when they were sick," they chuckled and wondered at the strange and mysterious ways of the East. Only in the 1940's did Britain and other Western countries come to so advanced an idea—socialized medicine.

The idea of preventive treatment is very old in China. A hundred years before the birth of Christ, a group of scholars wrote: "A skillful doctor cures illness where there is no sign of disease, and thus the disease never comes." And in another Chinese medical classic it is noted: "It is more important to prevent illness than to cure the illness when it has arisen."

Early Chinese physicians recommended that every traveler and every family keep certain basic medicines and that they have a book or two telling them how to use emergency medications. The government maintained sanitation inspectors and officials whose job was to exterminate vermin. If these officials used magic as well as potions and evil-smelling smokes in their work, the principle still was a sound one in behalf of public health. The sanitation police were also charged with the removal of corpses of men and animals from the roads and public places.

The most important medical classic of old China, *The Huang Ti Nei Ching, Su Wèn* (*The Yellow Emperor's Treatise on Internal Medicine*) deals fully with the responsibility of the medical corps not only to treat the sick, but to keep healthy people healthy. In this period the Chinese showed a deep appreciation of the problems of the mind in controlling the body, they appreciated fully the psychosomatic causes of many illnesses, and cautioned that one rule of good health was to be sure that: "Anxieties must at all cost be moderated."

These ancient doctors of China had embraced the basic idea of gymnastic exercises which the Chinese still hold in high esteem. "Running water does not become stale nor does a door pivot ever get worm-eaten," was an aphorism in the time of the Three Kingdoms. Chinese boxing, which has much of the element of dance, is also very old.

The importance of diet in health was recognized in China long before this could be said of Europe, and the Chinese of old were conscious of the relationship between pure drinking water and disease prevention. Covers were made for wells. They were cleaned regularly, and then locked to keep "insects and rats from falling into them, not to speak of people's children." In some cases devices like our modern sand filters were used to purify water.

The Chinese, besides developing a tasty national cuisine —or a group of them—paid a great deal of attention to cooking for health reasons. They did not like to eat cold food and knew that by eating hot foods they minimized the dangers of stomach infections and other diseases passed through foods. They practiced personal cleanliness to a remarkable degree. Half a millennium before the birth of Christ, the etiquette of a gentleman, as written down in the Li Chi, demanded that he wash his hands five times a day, take a bath every fifth day, and wash his hair every third day. With the coming of Buddhism, after the second century of the Christian Era, the bathhouse arrived in China, not just for the upper classes but for common folk as well, and in bathing and washing the Chinese used detergents, not soaps, from the beginning of history. They also brushed their teeth with tooth powder.

There are many other examples of technological and scientific achievement in ancient and medieval Chinese society. The Chinese used paddle wheels to propel their boats during the seventh century, when Europe lived in squalor. They knew the true nature of fossils—in other words, they had among them paleontologists.

If the Chinese were so far advanced, then why did they not go even further and develop modern science as the Western world was to do in the sixteenth and seventeenth centuries? It has been suggested that the basic differences in types of culture were responsible: that Chinese culture—which was agrarian and dominated by the state—did not have the goading force behind it that Western culture was to have. Western culture was a business culture, dominated by the search for wealth. The Chinese understood mechanics, hydrostatics, ballistics, pumps, and other devices, but they did not use them to become a shipping nation, to build their vast canal system, to build weapons fired by gunpowder (except of a very minor type) or pumps to support mining. The Chinese needed astronomy more than any other civilization—but they never developed their mathematics sufficiently to bring the calendar up to the standards of Egypt, for example.

In other words, the Chinese never brought to a point of combination the disciplines of mathematics and natural history that the West was to fuse.

CHAPTER 3

Science in Ancient Egypt

THERE were three great civilizations·in the world of ancient times, and while it is usual to compare their varied findings and discoveries, the civilization of China had little direct effect on the Western world. The civilization of Egypt seems to have had the most effect, although Babylonian influence should not be discounted. It is important to remember when considering Babylon and Egypt that the two civilizations grew up side by side but on quite different bases. Equally important is the fact that Egypt's scientific development came to a halt before the time of Christ, while the Chaldeans of the Fertile Crescent were engaged in a surge forward that translated itself directly into later Greek activity.

Egyptian civilization began about 3400 B.C. That is as far back as we can trace it—to the first dynasty of the Old Kingdom. Before that time, Egypt lived in what is called an Upper Stone Age society. The difference between the two, as with all societies, comes at that point where historians can be sure of dates and facts. Before 3400 B.C., Egyptians had developed a form of pictographic writing and were not simple savages. They cultivated barley, a kind of wheat, and raised flax from which they wove linen. They wore clothing—not skins—and they lived by a calendar.

The Egyptian calendar was the result of Egyptian astronomy, and while the Babylonian systems of astronomy and mathematics were superior to those of Egypt, the civilization of the Nile developed a good calendar quite early.

The ancients of this land were confirmed star watchers. In myth they saw the heavens as an area surrounded by the body of a goddess whom they called Nut, and they singled out a number of constellations for star watching. They also divided a belt of the sky along the equator into 36 parts, which could be observed in sequence during successive 10-day periods or decads. At first they divided their year into 12 months of 3 decads each—and kept track of its passage through the examination of the heavens. Eventually they added a holiday season of five days, to bring the year up to its actual total of 365. It was not long before they learned that the total year was really 365¼ days, if they were to reckon, year after year, on the rising of the star Sothis, the brightest in their sky. This meant that at the end of 4 years there was a difference of a whole day, and after 40 years a difference of 10 days. Thus the Egyptians built their calendar, later called the Sothic calendar, which in 45 B.C. was to be introduced to Rome by the conquering Julius Caesar and to form the base of the calendar the Western world uses today.

One reason for the accuracy of the Egyptian calendar was that the annual overflow or flooding of the Nile

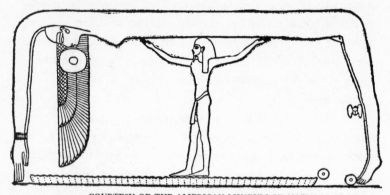

Shu, standing on the Ocean, supports Nut, the sky

almost always began at the same time as the rising of
Sothis. Practically no rain falls in Egypt. The land is a
vast desert spotted by a few handfuls of oases, but in its
length from north to south bisected by the green growth
that faces the cooling waters of the great river. Thus the Nile
was the life blood of Egypt, and if it failed to supply
enough water or supplied too much or if the farmers
failed to ready themselves to suit its whims, inevitable
poverty and famine would result.

The Egyptians also made tables of star risings and settings. They developed gnomons and ingenious sundials.

The civilization of Egypt was better known for other
scientific developments than for those of astronomy or
the mathematics of astronomy. Their most significant
invention was the pasting together of strips of the pulp
of a reed that grows in the delta of the Nile to make
papyrus—a smooth, flexible writing surface. Once
these sheets or rolls were pressed, soaked, and burnished
to flatness, they made an excellent tool for the transmission

of knowledge. Papyrus was far better than the clay tablets of the Babylonians and their forebears because it was portable and scrolls could be made of it—meaning that a complete work could be transcribed on a single sheet and kept easily in one place.

The invention of papyrus led to other inventions such as ink and fine writing brushes made of a rush that also grows in the Nile delta marshes. The papyrus was so satisfactory a writing material that it continued in use from 3000 B.C. until the eleventh century of the Christian Era. Both paper and parchment became available around the time of the birth of Christ.

COURTESY OF THE AMERICAN MUSEUM OF NATURAL HISTORY

A shaduf, used on the Nile for irrigation of lands above the water level

Papyrus led to the invention of quite a different type of writing than that used by the people of the Fertile Crescent. When one had to write by impressing soft clay even as it hardened, there was little time for niceties. When one could write with a brush on a piece of papyrus, much more speed and more variations in strokes were possible.

Writing in Egypt predated papyrus and had much the same basic background as that of Babylon and China. In each country it began with pictographs. So similar were these that one nineteenth-century historian and student of hieroglyphics studied them all from the Chinese point of view. A century earlier a French student of Chinese culture had made a flat claim that China had originally been an Egyptian colony and that Chinese characters were derived from the Egyptian. As was later discovered, this was nonsense, but it illustrates the similarities in pictographs in the beginning.

These similarities soon began to die out as the pictographs of Egypt and the other lands changed. At first Egyptian sculptors carved their hieroglyphics in stone, creating lasting statements that were also works of art in themselves. But as the scribes began to use papyri they changed the writing form. The old hieroglyphics—which stood first for words, then as symbols—were converted to a cursive writing called hieratic. That again proved too slow and was replaced by a kind of shorthand called demotic script.

Writing in Egypt as well as in the other lands was developed in the service of the rulers and the priesthood to keep track of taxes and the ownership of lands and similar vital statistics. But as time went on, the availability of

material caused men to keep other records, and long rolls
were put together. They were called *volumen,* a word we
have brought down to modern times in our own word
volume. Some of the preserved papyri are 18 inches wide,
and one is 133 feet long. These papyri deal with medical
matters, mathematics, and literature. From them and
from the tomb paintings and carvings in Egypt, the Western world has gained a good insight into the lives of
Egyptians.

Writing and writing materials, then, can be noted as
vital to the development of science, and the preservation
of ancient writings shows that many of the old Egyptians
adopted a scientific approach to life. Such a picture of the
ancients is a far cry from the portrait of the nineteenth
century, which showed Egyptians, Babylonians, and the
others as little more than savages.

Egyptian technology and mathematics were so advanced
and forceful in some areas that modern men have never
completely understood the Egyptian mastery of certain
materials and techniques. For example, in the building
of the pyramids at El Gîzeh, the Egyptians accomplished
marvelous feats. The greatest of these three structures,
the pyramid of Cheops, was built in the fourth dynasty
in about 2900 B.C. It was 480 feet high, and each side
measured 775 feet. It was, and is, one of the largest structures ever erected by man in any age. Imagine, if you can,
the feat of building a pyramid. The Egyptians seem to
have known only the first three of the following six
mechanical advantages that existed in the world at this
time: the lever, the inclined plane, the wedge, the wheel,
the pulley, and the screw.

Imagine, also, building a pyramid without the use of

the wheel or without any kind of a hoist. The pyramid consists of 2,250,000 blocks of stone of an average weight of 2.5 *tons each*. The men who worked in the quarries used chisels, but not as much as they used hard pieces of rock to pound a channel around and under the piece of wanted rock.

The huge blocks were transported to the site of the pyramid on sledges pulled by hundreds of men. The following is apparently the method used to erect such pyramids as those at El Gîzeh:

A ramp was built of earth. The blocks could be pulled up that ramp toward the bed of the pyramid. As the wall of the pyramid rose the blocks were lined up and fitted together. Their tops were made even, and they were put in place. Here chisels were used, as well as the mason's square and the plumb bob. It would have been impossible to slide the huge blocks across one another without something to ease the friction, so the Egyptians coated the lower block with a thin layer of wet mortar, and slid the upper block across that as easily as one slides on a soapy kitchen floor. The mortar was not needed to hold the blocks together because they were so closely placed that no filling of cracks or bonding was considered.

But how was the pyramid built? Historians can say and have said that it was built by thousands of men working for years and years. Then how were these men fed, clothed, housed, paid, and recruited? It would be no mean task for a twentieth-century Western society. And consider the marvelous accuracy of the measurements of the pyramid. Flinders Petrie, the Egyptologist, once remarked that the work of the Egyptian pyramid builders "is more like the work of opticians than of masons." He was referring to the minimal error in proportions—one part in four thousand.

The Ancient Egyptians also cut huge granite obelisks out of the cliffs at Aswan, transported them downstream, and erected them with precision. Considering the fact that they did not invent the grooved wheel or pulley, this was also a remarkable accomplishment. One of the obelisks, built for the temple of Karnak at Alexandria, weighed 455 tons. The Egyptians had even grander plans. An obelisk of 1,168 tons was cut from the rock at Aswan, but when it showed signs of breaking it was abandoned. Apparently the architects and engineers of Egypt had no fears about handling so large a piece of stone; they seemed to know what they were about.

Egyptian skills in the movement of huge masses of material showed a knowledge of practical arithmetic and geom-

THE METROPOLITAN MUSEUM OF ART
ROGERS FUND, 1912

Fragment of an inscribed Egyptian sundial

etry but their use of mathematics was limited to the most practical lines; they did not develop geometry or algebra. The Egyptian manner of solving mathematical problems was odd, but the results were quite often accurate within a very small degree, as can be seen in the pyramids and other remaining structures. The men who worked with mathematics transcribed their findings and their rules for later men to see. One such transcription was in the Rhind papyrus, a roll that dates back to the seventeenth century B.C. The Rhind was written by a scribe named Ahmose, who regarded his treatise on Egyptian mathematics as a system of rules for inquiring into nature. The papyrus gives a table governing fractions— fractions unlike those we use today for the most part. It contains forty arithmetic problems concerning division, multiplication of fractions, and quantity problems; the final portion deals with areas and volumes and shows practical, if imperfect, understanding of some aspects of geometry.

One would hardly say that this was higher mathematics, and the same thing could be said of Egyptian attempts to work at science. Dr. Derek Price, in his *Science Since Babylon,* refers to "scientific fumblings of the Ancient Egyptians." In mathematics, the Egyptians solved simple equations—but not with algebra. H. J. J. Winter remarks, in *Eastern Science,* that one must not indicate that the Egyptians possessed too great an understanding of abstraction. This warning can refer to works other than mathematics.

In technology the Egyptians ranked high. Some of their linens were so finely woven that they could hardly be distinguished from silk. In the sixteenth century B.C., the

Egyptians were adept in the manufacture and coloration of glass. They used copper and bronze, but not iron. They worked extensively with gold, which we can tell by seeing the intricate ornaments found in the tombs of some of the ancient Pharaohs. They had instruments—particularly important ones relating to architecture and construction —such as the inclined plane, the roller, the drill, the level, and plumb line. These were technical devices, not scientific ones as we know them, but they reflected beginnings for scientific study. The Egyptians were not the intellectual equals of the Babylonians, at least in mathematical sciences. But if one considers Egyptian civilization in terms of its arts and medicine, then Egypt can be more greatly admired. The period from the twentieth to the seventeenth century B.C. marked the climax of Egyptian scientific efforts, while the political climax came five centuries later. This was perhaps due to the peculiar nature of the Egyptian civilization, in which the distinction between subjective and objective ideas had little meaning. The position of the Pharaohs, state religion, and a preoccupation with everlasting life (which led to mummification of bodies to preserve them)—these worked against the development of a scientific objectivity, but they also worked for the creation of a refined medical knowledge, and Egyptian medical knowledge was of a remarkably high caliber.

The history of medicine seems to begin in the land of the Nile. It might be presumed that mummification to save the body for the afterlife was the principal reason for the leadership of Egypt in medicine, since mummification began in prehistoric times. But this was not so. Physicians did not prepare bodies for burial; technicians

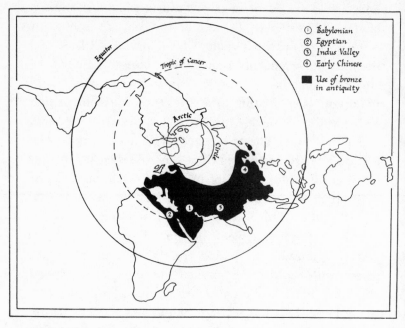

① Babylonian
② Egyptian
③ Indus Valley
④ Early Chinese

■ Use of bronze
in antiquity

Map showing areas in which bronze was used by ancient civilizations

did this. They learned to draw the brain out of the skull cavity through the nose, to remove much of the viscera (but not all) and place them in jars for preservation. They filled the body cavity with spices and soaked it in a preservative solution for about two months, then dried the body, covered it with an embalming paste, and wrapped it in linen bandages.

In the beginning of Egyptian history, the mineral substance natron was used to dry out the body, much as fish are salted to preserve them. Mummification was a religious rite performed to prepare the body so that the soul could return to the world of the living if it wanted to do so.

The Egyptians knew that the body would decompose unless it could be preserved.

Around 2000 B.C., mummification was more elaborate than simple "salting." An incision was made in the side of the body, and the liver, lungs, stomach, and other viscera were removed and put in sacred jars that were usually sealed and buried with the body. The heart was taken out, washed and bandaged, and put back inside the body. The cavities left by removal of the inner organs were stuffed with bandages soaked in resin.

These processes became more and more refined. Herodotus wrote of three classes of mummification. The most costly involved removal of the brain and the viscera. The body cavities were then filled with myrrh, cassia, and other aromatic substances, and after treating with natron, the body was washed in cedar oil and wrapped in bandages. A cheaper class called for an injection of cedar oil instead of removal of the viscera. The cheapest class called for removal of the viscera, but substitution of a less expensive oil than cedar.

Some surgical operations were known to the early Egyptians, although they did not use the trephination process of opening the skull nor did they amputate arms or legs. From prehistoric times, Egyptians practiced circumcision, but this was a priest's task rather than a physician's. The surgeon, generally speaking, used bronze instruments and was concerned with wounds. Surgeons tried to tie wounds together with an adhesive plaster, to reduce scars, but they expected wounds to suppurate.

A physician was also a magician, at least in the earliest days of Egyptian history. Many diseases were believed to have come from a demon who entered the patient's body, and the best possible method of getting it out was to cast a spell on it. Papyri have been preserved which give detailed instructions for such spells, beginning with an invocation such as: "Get thee hence, thou breaker of bones." The magician sometimes placed his hands on the patient; sometimes he held his seal above the patient's head; sometimes he drew a magic circle about the patient's house. He might prepare an image or a charm to be worn by the patient. From the tombs of some ancients, it seems that there were many kinds of specialists among physicians, at least among those who served the Pharaohs. One was called the "palace eye physician" and another the "palace stomach-bowel physician." And a jawbone found in a Fourth Dynasty tomb shows that around 2800 B.C. a doctor pierced a man's jaw to drain an abscess under a molar.

Some seven papyri dealing with medical matters have been discovered by Egyptologists. Two of the early ones, the Kahun and Gardiner fragments, deal with diseases of women, children, and cattle—dating back to 2000 B.C. Another, far more complete, is the Ebers, which deals with medical matters and gives 877 recipes concerning diseases and symptoms. The writer discussed diseases of the eye, skin, internal organs; diseases of the head, and especially the tongue, teeth, nose, and ears; diseases of women, and diseases of the extremities. This papyrus also contains material on anatomical matters and other medical affairs, but it also deals with cosmetics and housekeeping—an indication of the difference in attitude toward medicine in this ancient period and that of our own Western society of the twentieth century.

The Edwin Smith surgical papyrus deals with surgical

procedures developed over the centuries, describing a craft handed down from father to son. Apparently much of this papyrus has been lost, because the arrangement is orderly but incomplete, ending with a discussion of the spinal column. The Smith papyrus is interesting as an example of practical medicine because it contains no incantations or magical nonsense. The writer dealt with forty-eight different cases, dividing them systematically for discussion: first he gave the title, then an examination, then diagnosis, suggested treatment, and a glossary of obscure terms that might have been used in discussion of the case.

Examination was conducted by talking to the patient, by looking, smelling, feeling, and by moving parts of the patient's body. Diagnosis ended with a statement by the surgeon. He would either treat the ailment and "contend" with it, or not treat it.

Historians are impressed by the matter-of-factness and soberness of these early medical texts and with the variety of drugs that Egyptian physicians found in their minerals, vegetables, and animals. They prescribed medicines that contained flesh, fat, liver, brain, gall, blood, and excreta.

The vehicles for liquid dosage of medicines were water, milk, honey, wine, or beer. Goose grease, honey, and fats were used for emollients. The quantities of drugs were specified in prescriptions, and it was obvious that care was used in dispensing medicines. The Egyptians, like many other ancients, used powdered deer's horns for many diseases. Sometimes this was used with the legs of a bird, the hair of a jackass, the dung of geese; sometimes with the dung of cats or crocodiles. The treatments sound fantastic, but hartshorn—as it was known—was a valuable medicine.

By distilling the shavings of horns, physicians achieved an ammoniated liquid; today's doctors use an aqueous solution of ammonia called spirits of hartshorn. In some modern medicines, calcium phosphate is used where the ancients used the calcium from deer's horns.

Many other herbs known to have medicinal properties were used by the Egyptians, among them dill, coriander, cumin, and caraway. Onions and figs also were used. The Egyptians made castor oil. The seeds of the castor oil plant were chewed up and taken as a purgative, and an ointment for sores was made from them. Altogether, the drugs known to have existed were used in more than 2,000 unearthed prescriptions—a strange mixture of practical, or rational, treatment and magic. For example, the treatment for earache was to salt the ear, heat it with good wine, scrape off the salt, and heat the ear with wine again —continuing the treatment for four days. This is not far removed from some eardrops made of spirits of wine and boracic powder prescribed by today's physicians.

On the other hand, the treatment for gout was almost entirely magical. Here, slightly simplified, is the treatment recommended in the London-Leiden Magical Papyrus:

> You make the man sit down; you place clay under the feet of the man, his feet resting on it. You ask the man, saying, "Has it hardened?" for three days. Thereafter you take an ant; you cook it in oil of henna; you anoint his feet with it. When you have finished, you take Alexandrian figs and dried grapes and potentilla; you pound them with wine; you anoint him and you blow on him with your mouth.

Here was the conflict which prevented Egyptian medicine from becoming scientific, as we know it. Unlike the Chinese, the Egyptians did not realize the necessity for proper diet as part of good health. Chinese medicine had a heavy emphasis on prevention of disease; Egyptian doctors used magic and the arts of physicians and surgeons. As time went on, Egyptian physicians were taken to treat the kings and ruling families of many other lands in the Mediterranean area, an indication of the leading character of Egyptian medicine in its own time.

One question often raised concerns the nature of such a civilization: Can the attempts of these ancients to understand the world around them be called science at all? Professor Sarton put it this way in his *History of Science*:

"May we not say that whenever the attempt to solve a problem is made methodically, according to a predetermined order or plan, we are witnessing a scientific procedure, we are witnessing the very growth of science?"

By that definition, the men of Ancient Babylon, of China, and of Egypt all worked in science and all participated in the growth of science when they applied reason and method to their attempts to understand the world around them. Accepting that definition, Ahmose—the author of the Rhind papyrus on mathematics—was a scientist, as were the authors of the medical papyri. All were men trying to instruct other men in a search for the truth.

One problem that has bedeviled historians and students of science is the huge difference in reason and method between Egypt and Babylon. Egyptian science—Egyptian civilization—was on the wane in the seventeenth century before the birth of Christ. Babylonian science—and civilization—was still prospering, and approximately 1,500 years later was to show an even more astonishing surge under the Chaldeans.

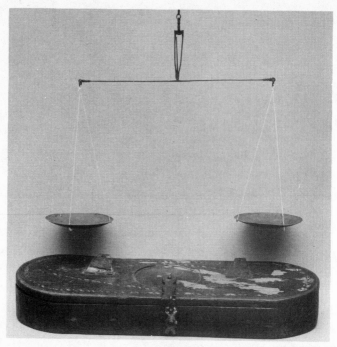

Egyptian bronze hand balance (scales) from the Coptic period

Historians attribute the fall of Egyptian science—or rather its failure to grow—to a combination of political and religious factors. The Egyptians became immersed in the doings of their god-kings and too little concerned with the progress of life on this planet. Otto Neugebauer, an authority on the sciences of the ancient world, has noted that mathematics and astronomy in Egypt never went beyond the most elementary limits, while in Babylon—where mathematics apparently preceded astronomy

—both were strong. He attributes the first decisive simpli-
fication of Babylonian mathematics to the evolution of
writing by professional scribes. He recalls the conquest
of Sumer by the Akkadians, who adopted Sumerian writing but made its signs correspond to their quite different
language. In other words, the use of Sumerian writing
forced the Semitic Akkadians to think in abstract terms.
Thus they could think in abstract terms in mathematics
and develop algebra, which the Egyptians never did.

The reasons for the differing roads of these ancient
civilizations are not yet thoroughly understood. As late
as 1923, when an edition of the Rhind Mathematical
Papyrus was published in the Western world, most of the
mathematical texts of the Babylonians had not been
found. The author of the Rhind book spoke of the
superiority of the Egyptians' mathematics over that of
Babylon. Since then, students of mathematics have discovered that the Babylonians were about 3,500 years
ahead of the Egyptians. What accounted for this change?
One scholar notes that it was the union, stability, and pros-
perity brought to Babylon by about 1760 B.C. that made it
possible for scholars to devote their lives to the pursuit
of learning. Other scholars say that since the land we call
Babylon knew practically no peace there was a constant
competition of ideas. They feel that this competition
led to the development of Babylonian science. The Egyptians excelled in the mathematics of measurement; the
Babylonians in the "more intellectual" pursuits of knowledge. The reasons for this are still relatively obscure but
it is quite certain that the Western world is indebted
to both societies for much of its cultural heritage.

CHAPTER 4

Stirrings in the Aegean

THE scientific and technical beginnings in what we call the Western world came down from the land of the Fertile Crescent and across the Mediterranean from Egypt. Between 2000 and 1500 B.C., when both primary civilizations were at a kind of cultural peak, a quite different civilization flourished in the Aegean islands.

The people of the Aegean area were sailors as well as farmers. They lived on a hundred little islands and in a hundred little seaports. Crete was a center of this civilization, and the culture developed there spread steadily throughout the islands of the Hellenic Sea. Little is yet known about the Minoan culture of the area. The Minoans had a written language, but it is not yet deciphered and may not be until some bilingual tablet is discovered that will allow translation of Minoan word symbols into some ancient language that scientists understand.

Like the Babylonians and the Egyptians, the Minoans had a highly competent technology. They built houses and palaces that were handsome and useful, although quite unlike those of other civilizations. They developed plumbing systems, using metal pipes. By 1500 B.C. they were using wheeled vehicles, including war chariots. The remains of a road paved with stones not later than 2000 B.C. have been found at Cnossus. Like the Babylonians and the Egyptians, these islanders learned a system of writing —in fact several systems, beginning with pictographs like those of Egypt and ending with a linear script.

Restored view of a wing of the Palace of Minos, Cnossus, Crete

This civilization had been lost to us because it was destroyed by other invaders. Two groups of invaders are important in the traceable development of Western science: the Phoenicians and the Hellenes.

The Phoenicians belonged to a Semitic race that had settled along the coast of what is now Syria, near Beirut. Their language was quite similar to that of the Hebrews.

The Phoenicians were conquered by the Egyptians and by the Assyrians, but they spread out along the coasts of much of the Mediterranean. When the Minoan civilization decayed, about the twelfth century before the birth of Christ, the Phoenicians began to compete with the Greeks for the mastery of the seas, and whereas the Greeks clustered around the Greek archipelago, the Phoenicians ranged wide, establishing trading posts and colonies that extended nearly to the end of the Mediterranean at the Pillars of Hercules. They built factories and colonies in Cyprus, Rhodes, Sicily, Sardinia, Libya, Tunisia, and at Carthage—most famous of all. They created a huge navy which roamed the Mediterranean, seeking battle with the Greeks and later with the Romans. They traded with East and West and contributed greatly to the interchange of cultures, but their one great contribution to Western culture was the invention of a workable alphabet which displaced the pictograph or symbol and turned written language into a mold much like the one we use today in our creation of words that have no pictographic importance.

The alphabet was as important an invention to the history of science (and to all learning) as writing. Before the alphabet, the art of writing belonged largely to priests and professional scribes. Egyptians had discovered the idea of expressing a single sound by a single sign, but they did not use it fully; cumbersome hieroglyphs continued to be used. But the idea that changed history was the representation of every sound of the language with as few signs as possible and without ambiguity—that is, without giving more than one meaning to a combination of signs. When the alphabet was perfected, a copyist or printer could reproduce words with the use of only some 20-odd signs. In terms of printing this was to prove revolutionary. Compare the English alphabet, or that of any Western language, with the Chinese pictographic system. A Western newspaper uses some 20-odd signs, plus figures and such special symbols as =, +, &, etc. A Chinese newspaper uses some 2,000 characters if it is to be read by the masses; more complex Chinese printed works may make use of 10,000 characters. While this system is undergoing great changes on the mainland of China today, it is still the basic system of printed Chinese. Comparison of such a system with an alphabet which makes use of some 20 to 30 symbols is obviously in favor of the smaller number.

The earliest evidence of the alphabet of the Phoenician type is found in about the seventeenth to fifteenth centuries B.C. in inscriptions of a group of kings of Byblos. This alphabet was made up of 22 letters, written from right to left, expressing consonants only. The Phoenician idea spread through Palestine, Syria, and Arabia. In Palestine, archaeologists have found a farmer's calendar written on a limestone tablet about 900 B.C. The Phoenicians also established colonies on the Mediterranean coastlines and thus brought their alphabet to Europe. Inscriptions in Phoenician script have been found in Cyprus, Malta, Sardinia, and at Marseilles. The Phoenician style also came to Greece. Greek originally was written from right to left, but after some years of confusion, the Ionic alphabet with 24 letters became standard. It was the most perfect written language for recording human speech that had been invented.

This Phoenician invention was passed to the Greeks, along with Egyptian and Babylonian mathematics, some

Minoan arithmetic, and astronomical ideas from all these nations. The process was continual and gradual, extending at least across two millennia, or thousand-year periods.

The earliest marks of Greek history date from about 1200 or 1100 B.C., the period in which the Trojan War has been placed. Our basic authority for the culture of the period is Homer, the unknown poet whose *Iliad* tells the story of that war. At that time there was no written record of his work, for papyrus and other writing materials did not become available to the Greeks until the seventh century B.C. That is not to say that there was no writing at all in the early Greek world, but writing was limited to inscriptions, records, and accounts. Minstrels carried the Greek world's literature from place to place, memorizing the long epic poems and songs. The *Iliad* and the later *Odyssey* may have been the creation of one man, two men, or more, but they are important to the history of science as well as to culture generally, because the two poems tell much of the life of ancient Greeks at the dawn of history.

The most important educational aspect of the Homeric poems is the fact that they taught Greek as one language, and even more important, that the poems became the cultural guide for all the people of the Greek regions. They established rules of conduct, honor, and social relations, not by preaching, but by citing noble examples. All Greeks honored this tradition, which is truly remarkable if one considers that they were not a pure race but a mixture of Aeolians, Ionians, Dorians, and others who moved into the area bounded on the north by what is now Bulgaria, on the east by the Turkish mainland (which was Hellenic territory), and on the south by Crete and Rhodes, an area which covered most of the Greek peninsula as we now know it.

Much of the material passed down in the Homeric poems shows the influence of the Minoan and Mycenaean civilizations that predated what we call Ancient Greece. Scholars still puzzle about the amount of the debt owed by Greece to Babylon, to Egypt, and to the earlier Aegean civilization of the Minoan period. They have made little progress in deciphering the signs, for they do not have all the tools, including such complicated devices as lists of early Greek words derived from foreign sources. Preparation of these lists is nearly a life's work and would be only the beginning of the difficult task of relating such words to scientific discoveries.

Myths and stories tell something of the tradition the Homeric Greeks inherited from the past. Cadmus, a celebrated mythical character and son of a Phoenician king, is supposed to have brought mining to the Greeks. When the Minoan civilization declined, Cyprus became a metals center for the Greek world. Early Greeks were aware of the soldering process and used it in metalwork. They knew the use of the level in building. The Phoenicians inhabiting the area now known as Lebanon were celebrated for their ability to bring water for long distances for irrigation, and while in the Aegean islands there was not so much need for this knowledge, much of the land of Greece itself is arid and rocky and irrigation techniques were welcomed.

The early Greeks knew a great deal more than many of us think about the uses of herbs and plants. They fertilized their crops with dung. Among them lived expert leatherworkers, weavers, potters, and smiths who worked in bronze and copper and tin. Later, when the Greek civilization, as opposed to the Aegean civilization, began to flourish, work was done in iron, for the age of bronze had passed.

In Homer some 150 words refer to the human anatomy and to medical matters, showing in outline how the ancient Greeks employed drugs, surgery, and medicine. Since these people were fierce warriors, they knew a considerable amount about the treatment of wounds. This knowledge came from three sources. First, it came from the tradition of the old Minoan culture which, though overthrown by barbarians, retained its nature until the time of the Greek invasions around 1000 B.C. From the Minoan civilization the Greeks drew the cult of the serpent, the symbol we still use as the emblem of modern medicine. Certain scholars suspect that the hygienic ideas of the Greeks were also drawn from the Minoans, who were experts in waste disposal and drainage. Second, from the Fertile Crescent the Greeks inherited and absorbed the demonic theories of medicine (driving out devils to cure disease) that were to be handed down to the Western world through medieval times. But they also drew upon the tradition of observation of physical details. The doctors of Babylon were careful in examination of the liver and other internal organs, and from this careful systematization came the Greek beginnings of a scientific method in medicine. Third, from Egypt the Greeks drew a knowledge of drugs, and the shape of early Greek surgical instruments shows that they followed the Egyptian pattern in making their medical tools. A sign of Egyptian interest in medical science is the deification of one of their earliest students of medicine. Imhotep, the chief minister to Zoser, Pharaoh of the third dynasty of Ancient Egypt, is celebrated as the first physician in history. He was made a god and was worshiped by a succession of Egyptian physicians after 3000 B.C. The Greeks inherited this tradition from Egypt; their god-hero was Asclepius, and through the worship of this God the Greeks also developed to a high degree the Egyptian system of treating the ill at temples—which was to evolve into the modern system of hospitalization.

In about the eighth century before the birth of Christ, another famous Greek poet was born in Cyme (a harbor in the Aegean, in the territory of the Aeolians) and taken to live on the Greek mainland in the area known as Boeotia. His name was Hesiod, and although he grew up as a simple farm boy, he was to become one of the most noted of all early Greek poets, and his poems were to be handed down as advice to his people.

One Hesiod poem, *Works and Days,* gives a collection of rules for farming and for navigation of the seas, considerable advice on ethics and religion, and a calendar of lucky and unlucky days. This poem seems to have been composed because Hesiod worried about the bad behavior of his brother Perses; consequently it is filled with advice. Hesiod tells the myth of Pandora and her box of evil spirits. He divides the world that was ancient to him into five periods: the age of Gold, one of peace and perfection, and the ages of Silver, Bronze, Minos, and the then current Iron Age—each of which saw the further decline of goodness. As to his own time, Hesiod saw goodness so far fallen that he looked forward to the end of the world altogether. Hesiod wrote other poems but most have been lost to our time, including one which

dealt with astronomy and mentioned several constellations, among them the Great Bear, Orion, and Pleiades.
So little of that poem remains that scholars know only
that it existed and that it explained the myths connected
with the constellations.

This fragment of history is representative of what
is *known* about the Greeks before the sixth century
B.C.—the point, roughly, at which scholars place the
birth of the Greek systems of knowledge and science.
It would be wrong to say that the birth of Greek
science (in Ionia, on the eastern shore of the Aegean)
came about in a vacuum. Egyptian science had declined
with the political decline of the Egyptian Empire. Babylon, as a place, had declined by this time, too, but the
Babylonian tradition had not, and the Egyptian tradition
was carried on by priests and artisans of the period that
lasted to the conquests of Alexander, and later, those of
Julius Caesar.

In the Fertile Crescent, the traditions of the Sumerians,
and even their language, were maintained by the Assyrians.
Their center of civilization was located along the upper
stretches of the Tigris River in what is now central Asia.
The first king of Assyria was Ashurnasirpal, in the ninth
century B.C. Others included Sargon I and Sargon II;
the ruler known in Biblical history as Sennacherib; and
Ashurbanipal, who established the capital at Nineveh
after Sennacherib destroyed Babylon. Ashurbanipal created
a huge library of clay tablets by sending his scholars to
the far reaches of his empire in search of the knowledge
of the old Sumerians and of the Semitic empires that had
followed them in the Fertile Crescent. In other words, the

Assyrians of Ashurbanipal's time were doing much the same kind of work that today's Egyptologists and Assyriologists do. The Sumerians were considered "ancient" by the Assyrians who edited, translated, and commented on the old Sumerian texts so that students of their time (and later times) might understand obscure references. Ashurbanipal's library contained books (the clay tablets *were* books, although not the bound kind we know) on history, astronomy, astrology, medicine, grammar, and many other subjects. If they did not influence the Greeks directly—and there is no indication that any Greek student of those times could read the Assyrian cuneiform—they did carry on a tradition which was to be important to the Greeks in a later time when Chaldean rule succeeded the Assyrians.

Chaldean science began at about the time that Ionian science was awakening—in the sixth century B.C. Speaking accurately, the Chaldean rulers controlled Babylon only for most of a single century. The first Chaldean emperor, Nabopolassar, allied himself with Cyaxares, the king of Media, and together they destroyed Nineveh and split the Assyrian Empire between them. Thereafter the Assyrian, and thus Sumerian, culture was continued in two regions: one of them the region of the Medes and Persians; the second the region of the Biblical tribes. But the term Chaldean science is loosely used to cover all the scientific tradition dating from the days of those Chaldean emperors until after the birth of Christ. What matters is that a continuing tradition of Fertile Crescent science and scholarship survived such vast changes in political management of the area. Here was

an indication that violence did not end scholarship when
rulers were wise enough to divorce politics from learning.

It is nearly impossible to explain the reasons for differences among men, but it is possible to show those differences. For example, in Babylon in the sixth century B.C.,
men were concerned with systemizing their knowledge of
the world about them. The Greeks were stirring in the
Ionian area of the Turkish coast. But in Palestine—the
land of the great religions of the Western world—there
was no such scientific stir. The Torah, the holy book of
Judaism, had been composed by this time. So had many
of the books of the Old Testament of the Bible, the books
of the prophets. The approaches of the people of the
land of Canaan and those of the Greeks were very different. The Greeks lived close to their gods and spoke
of them familiarly. The Hebrews lived in awe of their
omnipotent God. Living such different lives, the Hellenes
and Hebrews had far more to separate them than race
and language. One group strove to understand the world
it lived in; the other group sought to understand the
world after death.

The Greeks of Ionia and the western shores of the
Aegean had contact with Persia, where another religious
group flourished in the worship of the god whose prophet
was Zarathustra. But they did not adopt this religion—
Zoroastrianism. The Greeks had communication with
India, where the Buddha appeared in the sixth century,
but the Buddha failed to attract the Hellenes.

The Ionians were conscious of the glories of Egypt, for
in this period when Ionian science was beginning, Egypt
enjoyed a brief return to cultural leadership. Toward the

middle of the seventh century B.C., Ashurbanipal launched a war against Egypt and defeated the Egyptian rulers of the twenty-fifth dynasty. For several months Egypt was a colony of Assyria, but a noble named Psametik attracted a number of powerful Egyptian lords around him and hired Greek and other mercenaries to help drive out the invaders. The Assyrians' lines of communication were long, they were not willing to devote major effort to such a war, and they were driven out of Egypt. Psametik declared himself Pharaoh and founded the twenty-sixth dynasty, also known as the Saitic dynasty. Psametik caused a cultural rebirth of Egypt based on the ways of the great Pharaohs of the past. He repaired the irrigation canals of the Nile delta and opened Egypt to trade with the peoples of the entire Mediterranean Sea. He favored the establishment of Greek colonies and of Greek quarters in his capital and other cities. Necho, the son of Psametik, engaged in wars against the people of Palestine and against Nebuchadnezzar on the Euphrates River. Necho is of interest in the study of science because of the attention he gave to technical matters. He discovered that a canal had been built 1,500 years before to connect the Nile and the Red Sea, and he rebuilt and extended it so that in the time of Herodotus two triremes (ships with three banks of oars on each side) could pass through its width side by side. The canal was never completed because Necho spent the lives of thousands of men (120,-000, says Herodotus), because his engineers feared that the higher elevation of the Red Sea would flood the Nile with salt water, and because an oracle predicted that if it were finished foreigners would lap over the land like waves.

There was much association between the Greeks and Egyptians of those days. Greek merchants apparently supported the government of the Saitic dynasty. Greek businessmen built the city of Naucratis on the Canopic branch of the Nile River, and that city became a commercial center much as Alexandria did later. The center of the city, the Hellenion, was decorated with Ionian, Dorian, and Aeolian devices and architecture. The Egyptian revival was to end a few years later when Cambyses II, son of Cyrus the Great of Persia, defeated Psametik III and made Egypt a Persian colony. But that was not to happen until 525 B.C.

The Egyptians traveled often to Miletus, the central marketplace of Ionia, located on the coast of what is now the Anatolian Peninsula of Turkey. Necho and his children sent gifts to the temples of Miletus. After he had defeated Josiah, King of Judah, in the battle at Megiddo in 609, Necho sent his battle garments to a temple of Apollo near Miletus, to be dedicated to that god, and Greek leaders worshiped the gods of Isis and Osiris, so close was the cultural affinity of the two religions.

Originally, the people of Miletus came from Crete, bringing with them the traditions of the old Minoan high culture of a thousand years' antiquity. Miletus stood on a point between two gulfs near the mouth of the Maeander River. It had four harbors, well protected by islands and rock promontories, a fresh-water supply from its river, and protection of every known kind. Farmers in the inland regions grew figs and flax and wool to sell in the seagoing marketplace, and although Miletus was not on the main caravan route from the east, many travelers came overland to visit the famous port.

It was the practice of successful city-states in these times to establish colonies in outlying areas, and it was a mark of the importance and wealth of Miletus that it built colonies as far removed from the home port as the Black Sea and the Nile River delta—at least fifteen colonies on the Black Sea alone. Miletus was the most successful of all Greek city-states; it was the richest market in the eastern Aegean Sea at a time when the Aegean was the center of the sea power of the Western world.

Such wealth brought with it considerable leisure and a desire for knowledge of the ways of other lands—if for no reason but to acquire respect and to exhibit conspicuous consumption on the part of the wealthy. Miletian ships and Miletian captains traveled to every port in the known world of the West. They returned home with fragments of knowledge in the fields of astronomy, mathematics, geography, cartography, and medicine. They also learned astrology and the tongues of many lands. Necho, King of Egypt, sent several Phoenician ships to sail around Africa in an attempt to promote the foreign trade of his rejuvenated land. The Phoenicians set out from the Red Sea and sailed south, as Herodotus reported, until autumn came. Then they put in to shore and awaited the harvest, taking crops and sailing on. Two years passed, and in the third year Phoenician ships came through the Pillars of Hercules, which guard the Strait of Gibraltar, and thence returned to Egypt. Herodotus did not believe that story, but the sailors of Miletus knew it and understood what it meant. For Miletus was the cultural center of the Aegean, as well as the trading center, and it was from this center that the tradition of Greek intellectualism was to begin.

CHAPTER **5**

The Science of Ionia

WHEN we speak of Greek science, we must not look for important applications of that science to human affairs, for there were very few such applications. In the matter of technology, for example, the Greeks never went far. Among the Greeks, science was largely a mental exercise, and so it is not easy to find practical application of such ideas as their new geometry.

Greek engineering works—such as water supplies, city plans, and drainage projects—show advances in technical knowledge over the earlier civilizations, but they are relatively few in number. The great Greek scientists for the most part divorced themselves from practical knowledge. Plato regarded those who wanted to use geometry to measure land (that is what the term means) as people who made mathematics vulgar. What was lacking in Greece, from the beginning to the end, was a union between pure science and practical application.

Greek legend is celebrated for the story of the Seven Wise Men, four of whom appear to be listed in every enumeration known to history. Thales of Miletus, a shadowy figure, is always mentioned; he is less shadowy than any other individual preceding him in the history of science.

Thales may have been of Phoenician ancestry, but he grew up in the city of Miletus and claimed it as his home. At an early age he acquired a reputation for wisdom. He is credited with such sayings as "Know thyself," and is known as the first of the Greek physiologists and a "kind of early Franklin." The last description is prompted by a story that Thales was one of the two Greek wise men who so feared the rise of the Persians in the East that he advocated the establishment of a general council of Ionian cities. He is also known in legend for having predicted an eclipse in 585 B.C. and for having used this knowledge to stop a war. But this is legend, not fact. What Thales might better be known for is his contribution in the fields of mathematics and astronomy. As a young man, he traveled from Miletus to Egypt where he was exposed to astronomy and Egyptian mathematics. To be sure, the astronomy of Egypt was not comparable with that of Babylon, but it is equally sure that by the sixth century B.C. the interchange between Babylon and Egypt was so great that the astronomy of neither country could be said to be "pure." In Egypt, Thales learned something of eclipses and much about the practical mathematics that Egyptians used to construct their buildings and to measure distances. When he returned home to Ionia, he brought with him an understanding of the need to develop geometric theories. Thus he was the first man in any country—as far as is known—to realize that it was more important to develop general principles, or *theorems,* applicable to mathematics than to solve specific problems by the use of geometric figures without general principles.

To Thales, legend credits several geometric theorems that are so obvious that it took little of his genius to discover them: 1. A circle is bisected by its diameter. 2. The angles at the base of an isosceles triangle are equal. 3. If two straight lines cut one another, the opposite angles are equal. He was given credit for formulating several other propositions, too. There seems to be no question that he was the founder of the geometric tradition in Greece.

Thales was a man of universal curiosity. He wondered about the world around him and tried to understand it by reasoning. He knew something of magnetism. He gave considerable thought to the nature of the universe, and tried to explain it in terms that he could prove through his own experience and understanding. He came to the conclusion that the original substance of life was water, that from water came all the things in the universe. He began to establish a way of thinking about the universe and the objects in it that was to lead to the principles of Western science. Immanuel Kant, the German philosopher, said that Thales, if he were the first man to demonstrate the property of the isosceles triangle, brought about a revolution, for this was the first step to be taken on the road of science. Many men, like Kant, have noted a starting point at which science began. It is interesting to note how many points of beginning there are in ancient times, which, when added together, build a scientific basis and tradition.

One should remember that these early students of nature in the Ionian region were not trying to establish a scientific system, because they did not know what *science* was. Instead, they were trying to determine an order for the universe. The modern philosopher Giorgio di Santillana says that the first Greek book on science was that of Anaximander of Miletus, a contemporary of Thales. The fragment that remains of this work states that the impetus of birth is also the cause of death, and that this is as it should be, for the two pay reparations to one another. Anaximander's was a statement of the life cycle he saw around him in the birth, growth, and death of plants and animals. But not all these philosophers and thinkers were totally immersed in their consideration of the universe. Aristotle tells a story of Thales that indicates how human was this first Greek mathematician in his desire for fame and wealth. One winter, knowing that there would be a bumper crop of olives in the harvest of the coming summer, Thales rented all the olive presses in his region, getting them at very low prices because no one else expected so good a crop. When time for the harvest came and presses were needed, Thales let them go to the harvesters, but only after exacting his price. He made a considerable quantity of money, and, Aristotle said, showed thus that philosophers could be rich if they wanted to, but that they had other ambitions. But it was in character for Thales, coming from a commercial center, to be a shrewd businessman as well as an intellectual.

Little more is known about Anaximander than about Thales, but much more is known about his accomplishments. He was a practicing astronomer. He used the gnomon, and while he might have invented it—as had been done by innumerable intelligent men—there was no need for him to do so, since the gnomon was known to the Egyptians and Babylonians and could easily have been brought across the sea in any direction. Anaximander is better known for his theory of the makeup of the universe. Thales had supposed that the world could be reduced to a primary substance—water—but he could not show how water was transformed into soil, rock, and minerals. Anaximander accepted the idea of an order in nature, as implied in Thales' water theory, but held that the primary substance of the universe was an intangible—not something one could see or feel.

Anaximander stated that this intangible substance was infinite, or endless, that everything came from it and returned to it, and that our physical world is the result of a detachment of a portion of the intangible substance that was separated into two opposite substances—hot and cold. The hot was a circle of fire which grew around the earth, as bark on a tree. The sphere was later torn away and became enclosed in other circles which formed the sun, the moon, and the stars. These circles were tubular and supposedly revolved around an axis through the center of the earth (which accounted for the apparent daily rotation of the bodies). Anaximander is also known to us because he drew a famous map of the world showing the Greek world at the center of Asia and Africa, and the whole surrounded by ocean. Anaximander believed that the first animals were created in water and later came to land. Man, he believed, derived from other animals.

Like Thales, Anaximander was a wealthy man. Some call him a "merchant prince," and lament the attitude of the Ionians these men represented; they had taken to luxurious living and vanity in the sixth century before Christ, and were ripening for conquest by the Persians. But despite their purple robes and prideful hairdos, the Ionians were to contribute more to the Greek theme before they were swallowed in Persian armor. Thales built bridges and compiled almanacs, using information that must have come from Babylonian science. Eupalinus, an architect of Samos, established a plan for digging an aqueduct through a mountain so that workmen approaching from two ends met in the center with an error of only 30 feet horizontally and 10 feet vertically although the digging was a kilometer in length. At the same time, King Hezekiah of Judea commissioned an aqueduct in Jerusalem, and so primitive were the methods of his workers that the tunnel zigzagged around the area, twice as far as was necessary. Eupalinus used simple geometrical calculations to plan his direct approach, showing that while the Greeks were interested in cosmic matters, a few were also interested in practical applications.

Although Anaximander, student of Thales for a time, had deserted the Ionian theory of physical relationships between the entities of the universe—including space—a contemporary of Anaximander's returned to the search. He was Anaximenes, who held that air is the primary substance of life—air that is breath and wind together. So Anaximenes introduced, too, a concept of sameness between things large and small—which was to gather almost magical properties in centuries to come.

Anaximenes is notable, however, for his cosmological theories more than for such refinements as the microcosm-macrocosm idea. He came to believe that the stars were placed on a rotating sphere. He was remembered for this and for his supplanting of the intangible substance as the universal with the tangible air.

Other scientific discoveries were being made on the Asiatic coast of the Aegean in this period. Anaximander is said by Pliny to have discovered the obliquity of the ecliptic—the angle at which the sun crosses the earth in its journey across the skies. Cleostratus, of the island of Tenedos near the Hellespont, divided the skies into twelve equal lengths of the ecliptic, in accord with the twelve signs of the zodiac. Thenceforth he could measure the risings and settings of constellations and stars and place heavenly bodies in the skies at night. This division of the sky into zodiacal areas had been accomplished earlier by Babylonian astronomers. The Greeks undoubtedly derived some of their information from the Babylonians, but Cleostratus should not be criticized for borrowing. He brought something new to the Greeks. He also established a calendric system based on an eight-year cycle in which he used the figure of 365¼ days for the length of the year—and added days every eight years, to bring the fractions into measurable periods.

Xenophanes, an Ionian who moved to the western Mediterranean in later life, discovered the existence of fossils and reasoned that at one time the sea had covered parts of the earth that were mountains and uplands in his lifetime. At Syracuse, he found the remains of a fish; at Paros, the remains of an anchovy; and at Malta, the fossils of many kinds of marine animals. He knew how they were made—the animal covered over with mud, the mud hardening, and the consequent preservation of the outline of the animal for millions of years.

If Miletus was the center of the Ionian culture of the sixth century, not all accomplishment belonged to the Ionians or even to the Greeks. Anacharsis, a Scythian prince from the north, came to Greece in the sixth century and studied the ways of the Hellenes. He invented a two-armed anchor, a bellows, and a potter's wheel—or at least he discovered their existence and brought these implements back to Scythia when he returned. Yet the Ionians led all others in this period, as is evidenced by the many versions of the tale of the Seven Wise Men. In each version some of the names are different, but generally at least four of the seven are Greeks from the Asiatic area, not from the West. Ionian technicians and philosophers built huge and successful aqueducts; they were the first celebrated bridge builders; and among them were many engineers of such skill that they were called upon to build for Egyptian, Hebrew, and Persian princes.

Thales and other wise men of Greece had been aware of the threat from Persia as early as the seventh century, but neither eastern Greece, softened by love of luxury, nor the Ionians could be aroused. Darius and his Persians began to march. They conquered the Scythians, and they turned south then to fight against Croesus in Lydia, defeating him in 546 B.C. Ionia fell under Persian domination and Miletus became a Persian colony, but when the leading citizens agreed to collaborate with the conquerors, Miletus was left more free than the other Ionian territories, and actually prospered as well or better than before. Science and technical skills were not forgotten after the conquest. In fact, Hecataeus of Miletus, who is known as the father of geography, was born at about the time of the Persian conquest and grew up as a Persian

subject. To Hecataeus, the world consisted of two huge
land masses which lay in an ocean. These masses were
bisected across the horizon by an almost unbroken sea
ranging from the Pillars of Hercules at Gibraltar to the
end of the Fertile Crescent. The Black (Euxine) and
Caspian seas were separated by a small finger of land
that included the Caucasus Mountains. Hecataeus talked
to sailors, merchants, and travelers in order to get his
information; he made no attempt to project that information in a mathematical way or to draw a schematic view
of the world. He was interested only in gaining an overall
impression. His outlines of the Italian boot, Sicily, Sardinia, and the African coast are quite accurate. He knew
the general course of the Red Sea, but not the shape of
Africa or of the existence of Madagascar. Because of the
relationship of Ionia to the area we now know as southern
Russia, Hecataeus had a far better knowledge of that
region than of western Europe.

In the time of Hecataeus the Ionian search for knowledge began to dwindle. The businessmen of Miletus
grew irritable under the Persians, and in 494 B.C. they
rebelled, but the Persians put down the rebellion and
destroyed the city and its glory.

So powerful was the influence of Miletus on the people
of all Greece, however, that the destruction of the Ionian
capital created exactly the opposite reaction to that which
the Persians had sought. They wanted to throw fear into
the hearts of the Greeks, and bring them to heel. Instead,
the Greeks united in their shock at the horror of the
destruction. In 490 B.C., they defeated one invading Persian army at Marathon. Ten years later, led by the Spar-
tans, they delayed another Persian force at Thermopylae,

and prevented a decisive victory for the Persians. On land at Plataea, and on the sea at Salamis and Mycale, the Persians were finally routed and sent home, never to invade Greece again, but the Ionian day of leadership was past. The seekers of knowledge had moved to other areas or were born elsewhere.

One such was Pythagoras, one of the most illustrious figures in the history of science in the Hellenic world. He was born on the island of Samos in Ionia. He traveled to Miletus, where it is said that he studied under Thales for a time before traveling to Egypt. There he spent a number of years in the study of astronomy, geometry, and the mysteries of the Greek religion, which involved a loose system of gods, goddesses and heroes who were sometimes interchangeable and who lived in close proximity—one might even say kinship—to the people of the earth. The Greeks were given to a practice of divination and astrology (which they inherited at least in part from the Babylonians) and to complex rites in worship of many gods, including a number of foreign gods. The study of this magical religion was important, particularly to Pythagoras, because it led him to the contemplation of the nature of the universe and to the formulation of ideas about it. His studies—astronomy, mathematics, and religion—made it almost imperative that he come to grips with the problem of cosmology—the nature of the universe.

Pythagoras studied in Egypt during the brief period of enlightenment under the Saitic dynasty. When that dynasty was overthrown by the military victory of Cambyses, and Egypt became a Persian province, Pythagoras traveled to Babylon, in the heart of the new empire, to see at first hand the works of the ancient astronomers, which had been so carefully saved by the Assyrians.

He studied, according to the fragments of biography that are known, until he was fifty-six years old. Then he wandered about the Greek Empire until he settled in Crotona, far to the west of the major Greek possessions, at the foot of the Italian boot. There Pythagoras established a "school" of philosophy—a private colony in itself. The people, both men and women, lived in a separate community and wore a distinctive uniform. Theirs was more than a school; it was actually a way of living—a philosophy or religion. The followers of Pythagoras believed in the immortality of the soul and the transmigration of souls into animal bodies—a belief not unlike those held in the Orient, although no one can say that the Pythagoreans derived their ideas directly from the Orient. Theirs was a secret society, so secret that most of its beliefs have not been handed down, and so secret that other colonists in the Sicilian countryside took exception to the Pythagoreans, and eventually drove their founder from Crotona into exile.

The importance of Pythagoras and his followers lies in their physical studies of the world around them rather than in their mysticism. Pythagoras is known as the founder of an important geometric theorem and for his work in arithmetic and astronomy. He was the first Greek to discover the difference between even and odd numbers—the fact that even numbers can be divided into two equal parts. He began experimentation with pebbles in the sand, arranging them in squares, triangles, and other shapes. He did not use the numerical system as we know it, for at that period in history there was no satisfactory

Western numerical system to symbolize his discoveries. He drew such figures as triangles and showed that a square based on the hypotenuse of the triangle equals the sum of squares based on the other two sides. He discovered that this was true, no matter what size or shape the triangle assumed, and from this Pythagoras or his followers formulated a theorem.

Pythagoras or some of those who came after him discovered that the interior angles of a triangle are equal to two right angles and that the sum of the internal angles of a hexagon divided into four triangles is equal to that of the interior angles of the triangles—and equals eight right angles.

The idea that the earth is a sphere is at least as old as Pythagoras. For a group of people who dedicated their lives and efforts to the search for such truths, it was not a difficult idea to grasp. While looking out to sea the Pythagoreans may have watched a ship coming in, from the time that they could see only the top of its mast until the ship drew near the shore and they could see all of it clearly. They may have speculated that the reason the ship appeared to rise out of the sea was that it came over a curve, and that if such a curve did exist, it must represent part of a sphere. These ancients were familiar with the spherical shape of the sun and the moon, and to them the sphere represented a perfect body. The idea of the perfection of the sphere, in fact, came from the Pythagoreans, who went to considerable lengths to try to prove their theory.

They believed that the universe was composed of spherical bodies—the stars and planets—and that these bodies moved along spherical paths. Pythagoras approached the world with quite a different attitude from that of the old Babylonians or Egyptians. He believed that the universe could be explained in positive terms; men of the older civilizations had been content to justify the universe as a vast mystery governed by the whims of supreme beings. That was a remarkable difference, for while the Babylonians, in particular, had been careful in their observation of the different positions of stars and planets at different times, they had never tried to create a total explanation for heavenly movements. From the Pythagorean idea that all the universe could be explained in terms of circular movement came the complicated structure of Greek astronomy, which was the parent of twentieth-century astronomy. Further, Pythagoreans helped develop the idea that there was a difference between the world of the heavens and the world of earthlings. The first, they said, was perfect and changeless, moving in circles. The second—the world they saw about them on earth—was everchanging, the world of life and death.

Among other experiments, Pythagoreans attempted to deal with the universe in terms of music. They discovered that the strings of a lyre, put together in various measurable lengths, would produce pleasant sounds. Perhaps Pythagoras was the inventor of an idea called harmonic proportion, which involved relationships of musical notes.

In the Pythagorean school at Crotona lived a number of seekers after truth who studied the human body and disease. The leader of these was Alcmaeon of Crotona, who studied the organs of the senses and who may have been the first man in Western history to undertake a surgical operation on the human eye. Alcmaeon is important for another reason: he and his supporters conceived of health as a state of perfect harmony and disease as an indication of the disturbance of that harmony. Cures were brought about by ending the disharmony.

Alcmaeon also held that the brain and not the heart, as had been thought earlier, was the seat of the senses and the center of man's intellect. He is thought to have discovered the Eustachian tube in goats and to have given indications of understanding the differences between the veins and arteries in humans (although, of course, he did not understand the circulatory system as such).

Another important physician of this same Italian school of thought was Philolaus of Tarentum, who lived about the middle of the fifth century B.C. Philolaus is known in astronomy and cosmology for development of certain theories and for his comparison between the world and the individual. He held that the world resolved about a central fire and that man's essence also lay in fire. The liver was given a place in human affairs second only to the brain. These theories formed an important part of the base of later Greek thought.

It is apparent that the important men of these times were seeking to understand how man lived and died and the nature of the universe, all as parts of the same problem. One of the later figures in this study was Empedocles of Agrigentum, who lived until the middle of the fifth century, and who is often regarded as closely allied to the Pythagoreans. Empedocles advanced a new idea about the composition of the universe. Everything, he said, was composed of four elements: fire, water, ether, and earth. He also held that health came from harmony of the elements and that disease was caused by their disharmony.

Empedocles has been characterized by medical historian Arturo Castiglioni as one of the great masters in the field of biology in ancient times. He was given credit, although perhaps not properly so, for freeing the city of Selinuntum in Sicily of pestilence by draining its swamps, and for helping the city of Agrigentum to eliminate insects by fumigation. The importance of these men of the Pythagorean school to the development of medicine lay largely in their application of the real study of nature to medical ideas, their philosophic reasoning, and their investigation of physical life. These ideas were not separate; the same degree of progress could be noted in other fields of scientific inquiry.

CHAPTER 6

The Golden Age of Greece

THE fifth century before the birth of Christ was the period commonly known as the Golden Age of Greece, and the center for this surge of culture was Athens. That city had not grown to eminence as early as Ionia or the colonies of Sicily and Italy, but it was there that the great thinkers and artists of the fifth century flocked; Athens had led the Greeks to victory over the Persians and brought a period of peace to the land.

The arts and literature flourished in Athens. The city was famous for architectural wonders, drama, government, poetry, and sculpture. Here, however, we are concerned with the seeds of science and scientific thought which were brought to Athens. These ideas did not exist in a vacuum, but the cultural attainments of ancient Greece are so many and so varied that there is no way to describe them in a sentence or even a paragraph or two. As with the later Renaissance of the fifteenth and sixteenth centuries in western Europe, scientific awakenings accompanied artistic and political awakenings, and no part of a culture flourished but what the whole culture grew in stature.

Many of the men whose ideas were to be important in the development of science were also prominent in other fields. Pythagoras, as we have seen, was a leader of a philosophical school first of all, a mathematician and astronomer second. Generally speaking, this pattern was common to the Greeks. Pericles, victor over the Persians, brought to Athens the last of the great Ionian philosophers, Anaxagoras, whose cosmological ideas were quite advanced. He saw the universe as a whole, with its parts—no matter how tiny—as parts of that whole.

The Pythagoreans, however, were far more advanced than Anaxagoras in astronomical matters. Although Pythagoras fell into disgrace, his ideas persisted and his school of philosophy was revived and perpetuated after his death. The Pythagoreans, led by Philolaus, developed a theory to govern the movements of the heavenly bodies. Philolaus suggested that the earth moved from west to east around a central flame which was the center of the universe. In other words, 2,500 years ago a Greek philosopher suggested that the earth moved in orbit. In ways other than that his theory was farfetched, but it must be remembered that the idea the earth was the center of the universe was challenged here.

The Pythagorean view also held that the motion of the earth was such that the same side of the earth was always presented to the sun. For that reason, it was believed no one ever saw the central fire, and that even if people lived on the other side of the earth from Greece, they could not see the central fire because there was another planet—on the other side of earth—which shielded the central fire, keeping pace with the earth and obscuring the fire.

The daily motion of the earth around the central fire gave satisfactory explanation to the daily rotation of the heavens. Theorists held that all the heavenly bodies moved around the central fire in the same manner as did the earth. All this had a connection with the notes of the musical scale, and it was believed that the most pure bodies were those farthest from the central fire, and that earth—the least pure—was closest. Here, of course, the Pythagorean theory became mysticism.

In the fifth century B.C., another important theory was brought forth to explain the composition of the universe. Leucippus of Miletus and Democritus of Abdera developed a theory which held that everything in the universe was composed of atoms, which were physically indivisible. In other words, the atom was the irreducible body. An infinite number of atoms existed in the universe, these men said, and they moved forever in an infinite void. They had always existed, they could not be destroyed, although they moved freely. Atoms differed in sizes and shapes.

The atomists held that life had developed on earth from the primeval slime, that the soul was composed of the atoms of fire, which was life, and that every substance and object continued to exist as long as the atoms were arranged in a certain manner. Death came or change came through disarrangement of the atoms, those indestructible atoms, which went on to create another substance or object.

Democritus was the best known of these atomists. He came from Abdera, a city in Thrace at the northern end of the Aegean sea. He decided, while a youth, to spend his inheritance on the pursuit of knowledge, and since his inheritance was a large one, he traveled widely—far beyond the Greek world. He spent five years in Egypt studying mathematics and traveled up the Nile River as far as Meroë. He went to Babylon and to Persia, perhaps even to India as some have suggested, on perceiving the similarity between the atomist theory and Asiatic beliefs. Philosophers in India developed atomist theories of their own in schools known as the Nyāya and Vaiśeshka schools, around the time of the birth of Christ. The Greek atomic theory was not the atomic theory we know in modern science, and it should not be confused with that theory; neither should it be ignored, for it brought about intellectual stimulation. The Greeks had no way, nor any real idea, of proving their theory—it was a philosophical tenet. Yet it was positive thought about the nature of the universe, and as such, important in the development of men's orderly processes of thinking about the world around them.

Athenian science was nearly scuttled by a system of beliefs which arose during the fifth century B.C., at the height of the impetus of inquiry. The system was that of Sophistry, a remarkable negation of all responsibility and enthusiasm for life. Protagoras of Abdera was one of the most famous, and most successful, of Sophists. He said that "man is the measure of all things," therefore there could be no such thing as absolute truth. The Sophists held that form was more important than content. They contented themselves with teaching rhetoric, grammar and manners, and modes of living that produced as little discomfort as possible. Had the Sophists conquered all, the spirit of inquiry would have vanished from the world.

But the Sophists found in one who was often called a Sophist their mortal enemy. He was Socrates, the great teacher of Athens. Socrates is sometimes regarded as an enemy of science, for he was said to have had no use for the study of astronomy—a waste of time, he called it. Socrates was concerned with man's relationship to society and the world around him.

There is an opposite view of Socrates. The methods of the old philosophers were wrong, their speculations were useless, their astronomy was often vague and foolish. They were, in a sense, bent on exhausting all the wrong avenues in the search for the right one, and Socrates' contribution in the fifth century before Christ was to condemn and humiliate those who held these ideas, effectively to destroy the mode of thought, and to make it possible for men to move anew, using modes he, Socrates, devised. He insisted on clear definition of terms, logical method, respect for duty and for law, and skepticism about things unproved. All these are fundamental prerequisites of true science.

Socrates, of course, left no writings of his own, but Plato and Xenophon, two of his students, transmitted the ideas of the great teacher, plus some of their own, to a later generation and to us. Plato, in particular, advanced the philosophical approach, but added to the ideas of Socrates a theory of the nature of the universe— it was much like the Pythagorean theory. Plato, however, did bring about several important changes in manner of thought. One was his view that astronomy did not conflict with theology, for in his view natural laws were subordinated to the authority of divine principle. Also, he took no notice, astronomically, of the stars, but confined his thoughts to the moving bodies—basically the planets of the solar system (and the moon).

In this century, besides the philosophers, a number of mathematicians, astronomers, and technicians of various kinds came forth with important ideas. Hippocrates of Chios (not the physician) was the great mathematician of the fifth century, and his field was geometry. He is sometimes called "the father of geometry" in the same sense that the other Hippocrates was the father of medicine. Hippocrates of Chios concerned himself with two mathematical problems that interested the Athenians, the quadrature of the circle, which he solved (incompletely) with the discovery of lunes which could be squared, and the duplication of the cube, which he solved by use of compound ratios. Equally important, this Hippocrates undertook to classify and bring together the elements of geometry—one of the first men to do so. In this he was a forerunner of the great Euclid.

In astronomy, we have already discussed several of the heroic figures of the fifth century, including Philolaus, whose expression of the theory of the central fire has come down to the modern age. Most important in Pythagorean astronomy was the overall view of the world as *cosmos*, an orderly system of the universe. These astronomers were the first to offer such a view, as well as the first to make an important point of the spherical nature of the earth.

After Philolaus, Hicetas of Syracuse theorized that the earth turns on its axis every day, and he seems to have abandoned the idea of a central fire. Other astronomers began to awaken to the possibilities that might be found

in physical observation of the heavens rather than theoriz-
ing. Meton and Euctemon of Athens undertook systematic
observations of the solstices. This was a birth of a new
scientific attitude for the Greeks, whose greatness had
lain in the broad, overall view of man, his surroundings,
and his fate.

Technology flourished in the fifth century in Athens.
Mining techniques were improved. Hippodamus of Miletus became the first Greek town planner; he laid plans
for the construction of the Athenian harbor at Piraeus.
Artachaies, a Persian, dug a canal across the peninsula of
Athos. Athenians gained knowledge of the geography of
the Mediterranean and of Asia and Africa, and Herodotus,
the historian, handed down accounts of the voyages of
many travelers, including his own extensive trips around
the world known to the Greeks. Herodotus is important
to history—and to the history of science—because he tried
to leave a complete and fair picture of the world of his
times. He was hampered by having little knowledge of
astronomy and no training in mathematics. Thus he confused fact and fancy, and erred in his reports of certain
scientific discoveries and practices.

The fifth century was important for its rhetoric and
the love of beauty shown by the Greeks, but it was also
important for the rise of a physician who was the great
practitioner of his art. The doctor was Hippocrates of
Cos, the most complete medical man in ancient history
(for in Greece of this fifth century could be found the
sum of the knowledge of the past in the Western world).

Hippocrates was born on the island of Cos in about
the middle of the fifth century. He came from a family
of physicians—for in earliest Greek times the arts of medi-

cine were handed down from father to son through an Asclepieion—one of the temple-centers at which the Greek practice of medicine flourished in an air of mysticism, closely allied to theology.

Very little else is known about Hippocrates the man. Much is known—and disputed—about Hippocrates the physician. Some students attribute as many as 72 books to him, books covering 52 subjects. Others give him credit for 76 books. All his books and most of those that deal with Hippocratic medicine, were written in the Ionic dialect, which was the literary language of Greece in the fifth century, and these books give a very good picture of the medical knowledge of the period. This knowledge began with the Asclepiads, half priests, half physicians, who clustered around the temples dedicated to Asclepius, the patron and god of medicine in ancient Greece. By the time of Hippocrates, however, the priestly mission of the Asclepiadae had given over more to physical healing, and Hippocrates was more doctor than mystic.

Hippocrates is known to the public as the author of the Hippocratic oath, the guiding vow of physicians since his time. The oath is worth repeating, since it shows how far advanced was the ethical practice of medicine 2,500 years ago:

"I swear by Apollo the physician, and Aesculapius, and Hygeia, and Panacea, and all the gods and goddesses, that according to my ability and judgment, I will keep this Oath and this stipulation—to reckon him who taught me this art equally dear to me as my parents, to share my substance with him, and relieve his necessities if required; to look upon his offspring in the same footing as my own brothers, and to teach them this art, if they shall

THE OATH OF HIPPOCRATES

I SWEAR BY APOLLO THE PHYSI-CIAN AND AESCULAPIUS AND HEALTH AND ALL-HEAL AND ALL THE GODS AND GODDESSES THAT ACCORDING TO MY ABIL-ITY AND JUDGMENT I WILL KEEP THIS OATH AND THIS STIPULATION ⚘ ⚘ ⚘ ⚘ ⚘

O RECKON HIM WHO TAUGHT ME THIS ART EQUALLY DEAR TO ME AS MY PARENTS · TO SHARE MY SUB-STANCE WITH HIM AND RELIEVE HIS NECESSITIES IF REQUIRED · TO LOOK UPON HIS OFFSPRING IN THE SAME FOOTING AS MY OWN BROTHERS · AND TO TEACH THEM THIS ART IF THEY SHALL WISH TO LEARN IT · WITHOUT FEE OR STIPULATION · AND THAT BY PRECEPT LECTURE AND EVERY OTHER MODE OF INSTRUCTION I WILL IMPART A KNOWLEDGE OF THE ART TO MY OWN SONS AND THOSE OF MY TEACHERS AND TO DISCI-PLES BOUND BY A STIPULATION AND OATH ACCORDING TO THE LAW OF MEDICINE · BUT TO NONE OTHERS ❡ I WILL FOL-LOW THAT SYSTEM OF REGIMEN WHICH ACCORDING TO MY ABILITY AND JUDGMENT I CON-SIDER FOR THE BENEFIT OF MY PATIENTS · AND ABSTAIN FROM WHATEVER IS DELETERIOUS AND MISCHIEVOUS ❡ I WILL GIVE NO DEADLY MEDICINE TO ANYONE IF ASKED · NOR SUG-GEST ANY SUCH COUNSEL · AND IN LIKE MANNER I WILL NOT GIVE TO A WOMAN A PESSARY TO PRODUCE ABORTION ❡ WITH PURITY AND WITH HOLINESS I WILL PASS MY LIFE AND PRAC-TICE MY ART ❡ I WILL NOT CAS-TRATE ANYONE · NOT EVEN THOSE LABORING UNDER THE STONE · AND WILL SHUN MEN WHO ARE PRACTITIONERS OF THIS WORK ❡ INTO WHATEVER HOUSES I ENTER I WILL GO INTO THEM FOR THE BENEFIT OF THE SICK · AND WILL ABSTAIN FROM EVERY VOLUNTARY ACT OF MIS-CHIEF AND CORRUPTION · AND FURTHER · FROM THE SEDUC-TION OF FEMALES OR MALES OF FREEMEN AND SLAVES ❡ WHAT-EVER IN CONNECTION WITH MY PROFESSIONAL PRACTICE OR NOT IN CONNECTION WITH IT I SEE OR HEAR IN THE LIFE OF MEN WHICH OUGHT NOT TO BE SPOKEN OF ABROAD · I WILL NOT DIVULGE AS RECKONING THAT ALL SUCH SHOULD BE KEPT SECRET ❡ WHILE I CON-TINUE TO KEEP THIS OATH UN-VIOLATED MAY IT BE GRANTED TO ME TO ENJOY LIFE AND THE PRACTICE OF THE ART RE-SPECTED BY ALL MEN · IN ALL TIMES · BUT SHOULD I TRESPASS AND VIOLATE THIS OATH · MAY THE REVERSE BE MY LOT ⚘ ⚘

wish to learn it, without fee or stipulation, and that by precept, lecture, and every other mode of instruction, I will impart a knowledge of the art to my own sons, and those of my teachers, and to disciples bound by a stipu-lation and oath according to the law of medicine, but to none others. I will follow that system of regimen which, according to my ability and judgment, I consider for the benefit of my patients, and abstain from whatever is dele-terious and mischievous. I will give no deadly medicine to anyone if asked, nor suggest any such counsel; and in like manner I will not give to a woman a pessary to produce abortion. With purity and holiness I will pass my life and practice my art. I will not cut persons laboring under the stone, but will leave this to be done by men who are practitioners of this work. Into whatever houses I enter, I will go into them for the benefit of the sick, and will abstain from every voluntary act of mischief and corruption; and, further, from the seduction of females or males, of freemen and slaves. Whatever, in connection with my professional practice, or not in connection with it, I see or hear, in the life of men, which ought not to be spoken abroad, I will not divulge, as reckoning that all such should be kept secret. While I continue to keep this Oath unviolated, may it be granted to me to enjoy life and the practice of the art, respected by all men, in all times! But should I trespass and violate this Oath, may the reverse be my lot!"

The same oath, with some alteration, remains the guiding spirit of the medical profession of the Western world, so aptly and completely did it establish an ethical concept of the art of medicine. But the Hippocratic physician of the fifth century B.C. did not rely totally on the ethical concept of his half-priestly mission for his successes. He knew a great deal about the human body, and about disease—not much, perhaps, in terms of the knowledge of the modern scientific age, but much in terms of the knowledge of Stone Age society, which was not far in the past for many men in many lands.

The Hippocratic physician knew very little about anatomy or physiology. His general knowledge was guided by a theory of "humors," following the theories of Alcmaeon. Doctors of the Cnidian school tried to diagnose special diseases; doctors of the school of Cos tended to group illnesses into one or two categories and showed more concern with the maintenance of good health than with the cure of disease (because they were better able to help people maintain health than to cure their diseases). When a man did fall ill, the Greek physician attempted to forecast the course of the disease, in other words to give a prognosis, and to help the patient understand what he would have to undergo.

The Hippocratic physicians understood fever, although they did not measure it as do latter-day physicians. They knew pneumonia, pleurisy, and consumption, and were familiar with several diseases of the eye, which appeared to be quite common. They were humble men, who knew how little they knew about the body and the diseases which affect it. Hippocrates used purgatives, emetics, enemas, bleeding, and starvation diets in his treatments. He also used baths, rubbing, wine, honey, and other materials. One of his major ideas was to take advantage of the healing power of nature, to try to assist the patient to let nature help. Historians call Hippocratic medicine scientific medicine. Probably it was the first scientific medicine practiced in the world. Why scientific? Because Hippocrates gave himself the task of solving problems of medicine in a logical manner. He was also aware of the psychological problems of illness as well as the physical problems.

Some of Hippocrates' books were written to be read by physicians. Some were written for the layman, especially those which gave instruction in hygienic practice and health measures. Hippocrates continues to be admired by medical men because he was precise in his treatment of case histories, scientific in his method, and unimpassioned in his approach to the problems he faced as a doctor.

Some of his writings dealt with surgery as well as with the arts of the physician. These Greeks were thoroughly familiar with trephining, with fractures, and with wounds caused by weapons, and Hippocrates even set down rules for behavior of the surgeon, urging his students to practice various manners of manipulation and other techniques. In techniques and scientific understanding of the human body the Hippocratic physicians possessed only the most primitive knowledge, by twentieth-century standards. Still, Castiglioni and other historians of medicine give Hippocrates credit for freeing medicine from superstition and directing medicine to its only goal, the cure of the sick. In the days of Hippocrates, the Greeks still believed in the miraculous cures that were possible at the temples of Aesculapius, and, although Hippocrates was a member of such a priestly family, he did not write about the miraculous cures granted to those who consulted oracles at the temples. He did not even condemn the practice of mysticism and magic, he ignored them, and expended his efforts in the study of physical medicine and the rules of practice. Thus Hippocrates, long before the term was invented, was a scientist.

In the following century, the fourth before the birth of Christ, Athens was lost (it had fallen in 404) but Hellenic science continued to progress. In this period Eudoxus of Cnidos invented a system of astronomy, sometimes called the first scientific astronomy, which attempted to explain the motions of all the celestial bodies, using 27 concentric spheres. Eudoxus had studied in Egypt and

was familiar with Greek geometry, and he attacked the
problem of heavenly movement in a mathematical way.

In order to work out the motions of all the celestial
bodies he knew, Eudoxus decided on the existence of 27
concentric spheres, each turning around a definite axis
at a definite speed. It was the first attempt to explain the
universe mathematically. His approach was not to question the actual existence of these spheres; it was enough
that by presenting his theory he gave an explanation that
was not in contradiction to the observations of astronomers through the ages. Some historians do not give
Eudoxus quite so much credit; indeed, three hundred
years later the astronomer Sosigenes wrote that the spheres
of Eudoxus did not account for actual heavenly movement, as Sosigenes knew it, and that they did not even
account properly for heavenly movement as Eudoxus had
known it. Nonetheless, the Eudoxian theory was accepted
by the school of students he led, and in a few years,
Callippus, one of Eudoxus' students, added more heavenly
spheres to account for vagaries of movement, bringing
the total to 34. Later another 22 spheres were added by
the great Aristotle, again in an attempt to conform the
theory to the movements then known to exist.

Aristotle was the central figure of another age of Greek
science; perhaps one might call it a third age, having
passed through the ancient Greek period to the fifth
century of Socrates and Plato. The period of Aristotle
was marked by political change and the emergence of
Macedonia, a region above the old Hellas, as the dominant force in the Mediterranean.

Aristotle was not truly a Macedonian by background
or race. He was born on the peninsula of Chalcidice,

Aristotle

which had been colonized by Ionians, but the territory
was so close to Macedonia (as Latvia was to Russia) that
it was annexed by the Macedonians when they became a
world power. Philip of Macedonia was the king who made
his nation leader of the Hellenic peoples. In a sense it
was fortunate for Aristotle that he was born in a territory that became a part of Macedonia, for it gave him
an entree to the court, and made it possible for him to
rise to eminence. He was born in the city of Stageira in
384, at a time when Chalcidice was still independent. At
least one historian places the works of Aristotle in sequence
with those of Plato—in doing so he shows how Aristotle's
philosophy diverged from that of Plato and the earlier
Greeks.

Aristotle's education began on Chalcidice, but when he was seventeen years old he was sent to Athens where he was to remain for many years. In the beginning, Aristotle was a student under Plato. Later, he grew away from his teacher, and still later he went to Assus, a city near Lesbos, and here he studied animal life and began to develop his own ideas about nature and mankind. In 343 Philip of Macedonia offered Aristotle a post as tutor to his son Alexander; Aristotle accepted and moved to Pella, the king's residence, where he remained for three years, teaching the boy who was to become the greatest conqueror in the history of Greece. The formal master-student relationship was ended in 340 when Alexander was forced to accept the reins of government as regent because his father was abroad on military conquest.

Alexander succeeded his father as emperor, and began to expand the empire. Aristotle, honored by the king, returned to Athens to found a new school, the Lyceum, which was begun in 335. Twelve years later, on the death of Alexander, Aristotle removed himself from Athens to his native Chalcidice, apparently to preserve his life against the enemies of Alexander who wanted no resurgence of Alexandrian power, and who found Aristotle suspect. In 322, Aristotle died in his home territory.

Of all the great Greeks, Aristotle was to be the most influential in the development of thought in the Western world. For centuries he would be almost unknown in Europe, as the line of Western development broke sharply and was not picked up again until nearly thirteen hundred years later. Aristotle then became almost Biblical in his impact on scholars of western Europe.

Aristotle's fields of study and his writings were almost

encyclopedic and it is thus, perhaps, that some of his fame has been preserved. But in his own time Aristotle was known better for writings and ideas that followed more closely on Plato's than those which were transmitted to the Western world at the end of the Dark Ages. Aristotle also had help, if not in his writings at least in his researches, from a number of students and associates. Only thus could he have accomplished as much as he did. This is not to be taken as negative criticism. Indeed, Aristotle was one of the greatest men in all the human past, and if his knowledge was imperfect, and his writings were partly the product of the work of others, the same can be said without derogation of many of the other great men of the world.

In the matter of astronomy, Aristotle came to believe that the spheres of Eudoxus, which carried their heavenly bodies around in orbit, were real, not just mathematical figures. Aristotle arranged the bodies in order, outward from the earth, according to their apparent periods of revolution. Thus the moon came first, then the sun, Venus, Mercury, Mars, Jupiter, and Saturn—the only large bodies in the solar system visible to the naked eye. He also believed that the outer sphere of apparently fixed stars was moved by a *primum mobile,* an omnipotent force at the edge of the universe, which governed all the spheres and all the universe, and that each sphere was controlled by a similar, but lesser, force of its own, spiritual in nature. The mover of each planet worked against the primum mobile; thus the planets each had their own west-to-east motion which was contrary to the daily rotation of the planet. Saturn, the planet farthest from the earth, had the greatest difficulty in overcoming the force of the primum mobile, so its rotation took longer than that of any other body. The moon, closest to earth, had the least difficulty in overcoming the force of the primum mobile, so its period of rotation was the shortest.

Aristotle divided the universe into two kinds of matter: that which existed in the heavens, and thus was pure; and that which existed on earth, and thus was impure. The earthly elements were earth, water, air, and fire. The most perfect were those farthest from earth. Fire was the most perfect of earthly elements, air was next, water was third, and earth itself was least pure. Of the heavenly bodies the moon was least pure, but all these bodies had perfect motion—circular motion.

In the field of physics—ancient physics concerned both animate and inanimate bodies—Aristotle held that a body could stay in motion only as long as it was in direct contact with a mover. A mover might be inside the body, or outside. A body such as a stone, thrown from a catapult, did not move freely. It was maintained in motion after it left the catapult by the air, which streamed along behind it to prevent the formation of a vacuum. Aristotle did not believe a vacuum could exist, and he disputed the theories of the atomists, who held that the world consisted of atoms in a void.

In the field of biology, Aristotle classified more than five hundred animal species, and he seems to have dissected a number of animals in studying them. He called attention to pecularities in the structures of animals, such as the fact that no animal he knew had both tusks and horns, because, as he said it, no animal required both for protection. He also observed that grass-eating animals (ruminants) had both multiple stomachs and few teeth, and he supposed that the ruminants were given complex stomachs by nature to compensate for the deficiency in teeth.

He began classifying animals. He noted that whales, which bore their young alive, were more akin to land animals than to fishes, which laid eggs. He also noted that four-footed animals which brought forth their young alive had hair, while four-footed animals which laid eggs had scales. Again, he brought his view of the universe into play to guide his thoughts on the animal kingdom. The various kinds of animals formed a continuous line, increasing in degree of perfection, from the most crude animals up to men, the most perfect in his eyes. He decided that the structure of an organism was governed by the quality of its soul. Plants, he said, had only a partial soul, which was responsible for growth and reproduction. Animals had a more complete soul, which governed the faculties of movement and sensation. Man also had a rational soul, seated in the heart, which raised him above all other creatures.

Aristotle's life marked a turning point in the history of Greek science, because he was the last to bring forth a system of the world as a whole, and the first to begin practical study of the world around him. The earlier Greek philosophers had theorized much but experimented little; Aristotle did the same in relation to astronomy, but his later works on zoology showed much close observation of nature. The idea of observation followed by judgment was a trend which was developed more thoroughly by Aristotle's successors. After Aristotle left the Athenian Lyceum he was succeeded by Theophrastus, who studied botany so extensively that many of the names he gave to plants survive in modern botanical language. Theophrastus recognized that reproduction in plants of a higher nature was sexual, although this knowledge was lost to later men. He also reacted against the philosophical approach to the study of the world, feeling that the scientist should explain what he saw around him in terms of the process observed in the mechanical arts. In other words, Theophrastus tried to lead his followers away from the search for purposes and final causes in nature, and to study the mechanics of nature.

The next head of the Lyceum, Strato of Lampsacus, carried out a number of experiments. He noted the difference in the weight of a piece of wood before and after heating it, and he discovered that although a piece of charcoal had the same volume it had possessed as wood before being heated, it weighed less. He explained it by stating that matter had left the wood. He also showed that partly emptied vessels, when inverted and immersed, would suck up water, and he decided that this was because the water filled the vacuums between the particles of air. Strato conducted many such experiments and followed the practice of observation and reasoning. He was, however, nearly the last of the students of science to be of importance in the Athenian Lyceum, for the whole emphasis of Hellenic science shifted away from Greece at the end of the Alexandrian age.

An interesting and important development occurred in medicine during the end of the Athenian period. Diocles of Carystus took up the study of medicine, under the influence of the two Athenian schools, the old Academy of Plato, and the newer Lyceum of Aristotle. Diocles began to reshape the study of medicine in Athens, tending away from the Hippocratic system, in a sense. He wrote in the Attic dialect, rather than in the Ionian (like later Europeans who chose to extend knowledge by writing in languages other than Latin). Diocles did not reject the Hippocratic teaching but chose to enlarge upon it, and in so doing formed a school known as the Dogmatic school. Dogmatism came to mean a decline in the practice of medicine, for the practice became stylized, rigid, and many students of medicine were more eager to follow the writings of the past than to use their own eyes. Diocles, on the other hand, examined embryos, made animal dissections, and studied childbirth and the diseases of women. But medicine, as such, began a period of decline in the West.

All Greece declined, with the end of the reign of Alexander in 323 B.C., just when it seemed that Greece would establish a new world order under Alexander the Great. He captured Persia and moved on against India, until forced to stop by the anger of his soldiers at being kept so long from home. Where Plato and Aristotle had held that all non-Greeks were barbarians and inferior by nature to Greeks, Alexander offered the people of captured territories equal citizenship and equal rights in his empire. He held knowledge in high esteem, established Orientals in high positions, married an Oriental princess, and encouraged his soldiers to marry Persians. He carried engineers and a train of students of nature with him on his war trail. Architects, geographers, surveyors, historians, and a young man named Ptolemy, the son of Lagos, accompanied Alexander. This youth was to become important later when he took over the imperial city of Alexandria and turned it into the scientific center of the world.

Alexander's death brought an end to more than an empire. It coincided with the falling away of Athenian culture from its pinnacles of the fifth and fourth centuries B.C. One of the greatest achievements of all the time before 300 B.C. was the body of knowledge assembled by Aristotle and his followers. Aristotle had gathered together the best of Western astronomy, physics, zoology, and had combined these with humanist studies and a philosophy of life. Shortly after Aristotle's death, the Lyceum and the Academy of Athens were challenged for supremacy of teaching by the Epicurean and Stoic philosophical schools, which glorified disillusionment with the whole of mankind and the world. The Stoics and Epicureans had little interest in the pursuit of science. They were more interested in teaching man to accept his fate and to live in the best society they could devise while he awaited death.

Still, by the end of the fourth century before the birth of Christ, science had come far. All of its branches had been established, except physics and chemistry. The Greeks and their forebears had asked all the great questions that we are still trying to answer today and had reduced the main issue among men to rationalism and irrationalism. True, Greece was declining in power and importance, but the spirit of inquiry the Greeks had assembled from the knowledge of the more ancient civilizations, plus their own way of looking at the affairs of mankind—this scientific spirit was to continue.

CHAPTER 7

The Rise of Alexandrian Science

For three centuries before the time of Alexander the Great the Greeks had been moving into Egypt. Under the Saitic dynasty which was established in 663 B.C., Greeks were welcomed to an Egypt that showed signs of rejuvenation as the rulers tried to recapture the glories of their ancestors. In the sixth century Greek colonies were established along the Nile River delta, and although the Egyptian people resented these foreigners, their rulers protected the newcomers, for the Greeks brought much that was valuable to Egypt, including learning and a highly developed trade in many goods. By the end of the sixth century the Greeks had concentrated in one city, called Naucratis, located in the western delta of the Nile River. They built there a city that was Greek in architecture and in all its planning and way of life.

The Greek settlers prospered, even when the Saitic dynasty was overthrown by the Persians, and they stayed on in northern Egypt to become firmly rooted there. History credits Alexander with having built Alexandria, but this is true only in the most general sense. Alexander did visit Egypt and did order the construction of a city there. But the city was actually not very far along in construction by the time Alexander left Egypt, and at that time the government was located at Memphis. The city named for the conquering Macedonian emperor was not actually completed until after Alexander's death in 323. The man who truly built the city was Ptolemaeus Soter, one of Alexander's generals and the founder of the dynasty of the Ptolemies, which was to rule Egypt until the days of Cleopatra, last of that line.

After Alexander had died of fever in Babylon and the city had been completed, this Ptolemy secured the great king's body and brought it to Alexandria where he had it buried in a temple called the *sēma*. Only then did the city deserve its title as capital of the Macedonian world.

While Alexander lived, apparently it was his intention to make Alexandria the capital of the civilized world, for he had plans to create "one world" by giving all men common citizenship. These plans fell rapidly in pieces after Alexander's death, as did his empire; the generals argued among themselves, plotted in small groups, and finally abandoned the common council, one by one, to seize and to try to hold various sections of the Alexandrian empire as individual kingdoms. Ptolemy's own choice was the land he had administered under Alexander, and here the pattern was set for intermingling of races, free movement and trade, and establishment of a great city and center of learning.

Alexandria was a planned city. The architect was Democrates of Rhodes, who also built the famous temple to

Artemis at Ephesus. He spared no expense in laying out the city, for he had been commissioned by Alexander himself to do the job before the conqueror headed east on his final journey. Alexandria was built on a spit of land that extended north into the Mediterranean and south to the shore of Lake Mareotis. It was built around two great avenues, one extending east and west and the other north and south, and the lesser streets were laid out to form squares. The city was divided into five districts. Its center was the Brucheum, which housed the Greek quarter and some of the most important buildings in the history of learning. Two of these were the Museum and the Library; the first was dedicated to scientific research and the second to the advancement of the arts and literature. The two institutions, created by the Ptolemies, also were supported by them. The Museum and Library were interdependent, for the collection of manuscript rolls was the job of the library, and many of these concerned scientific matters.

Ptolemy created the Museum to maintain and advance Greek culture; even the name in Greek indicates a comfortable mixture of religion, mysticism, and learning under which Greek science grew so well. A museum is a temple of the Muses, the nine patron goddesses of knowledge, who were also daughters of Zeus, the principal god of the Greeks. The Museum occupied several of the buildings near the sea, and the scholars Ptolemy brought to Alexandria from the far corners of the Hellenic regions lived together there, not as in a college, but as in a research institute, instructing their assistants and privileged apprentices without holding formal classes. The Museum included an astronomical observatory, a room for dissection of corpses and the study of anatomy, the Library, and gardens for the study of botany and zoology.

The first important scholar to come to the Museum was Demetrius of Phalerum, once governor of Athens, who had been forced into exile in 307 B.C. He came to Alexandria at the invitation of Ptolemy. His personal collection of books became the nucleus of the Alexandrian Library. He was, then, the organizer of the Museum and Library in a scholarly sense, but he was not particularly scientifically inclined. The scientific cast to the Museum was brought by Strato of Lampsacus, tutor of Ptolemy's son, who eventually left Alexandria and returned to Athens to direct the famous Lyceum during the last days of his life. Strato is given credit for persuading Ptolemy to make the Museum a scientific institution. Here, for the next two hundred years the impetus for progress of science would be centered. After that time the Museum would gradually decline, as rival institutions in Rhodes, Constantinople, and Athens sought to achieve leadership in culture. But throughout the period of Hellenic influence the Museum was to have some importance, until it was brought to ruination by the murder of Hypatia, daughter of Theon and a scientist in her own right, by a Christian mob that stormed the Brucheum in 415 A.D. Before its decline, the Museum had a staff of some one hundred scientists and professors, paid by the emperor's treasury, and the Library housed some half million papyrus rolls.

One of the first great geniuses to work at Alexandria was also to become one of the best known to modern times—Euclid, the mathematician. Euclid came to Alexandria while the first Ptolemy was alive. Apparently he had no direct connection with the Museum, but in Alexandria he formulated the work that became his *Elements of Geometry*, the synthesis and extension of the work of all the great mathematicians of the Greek past. He compiled a work of thirteen books, the first six dealing with plane geometry, the next four dealing with arithmetic and the theory of numbers, and three final books on solid geometry. In the first books he also dealt with geometric algebra.

Euclid worked in Alexandria at about the beginning of the third century B.C., as did several astronomers, among them Aristarchus of Samos, although it is not positive that Aristarchus worked in Alexandria. (The uncertainty is brought about because Aristarchus was a pupil of Strato, but whether at Alexandria or at Athens has not been settled.) Aristarchus made the first scientific attempt to measure the relative distances of the sun and the moon from the earth. He supposed that at the time of the half moon, the sun, moon, and earth would form a right triangle (with the earth at the center), and that the relative distances between the sun and earth and the moon and earth could be determined by measuring the angle of separation. He measured it as 87 degrees, and calculated that the sun was nineteen times as far from earth as the moon.

He also noted that the moon, during an eclipse of the sun, just covered the sun's image. He concluded that the sun was nineteen times as large as the moon, and, thus, being nineteen times the size, they would appear at those distances to be the same size. He measured the breadth of the earth's shadow during eclipses of the moon, and stated that the diameter of the earth is three times that of the moon. Thus, he said, the diameter of the sun must be six or seven times as large as that of the earth.

Most important about Aristarchus is the fact that he adopted the Copernican view of the universe eighteen hundred years before Copernicus. Toward the end of the third century before Christ, Archimedes, a younger man, wrote that Aristarchus had claimed that the universe was much larger than it was generally believed to be, that the sun remained unmoved, and that the earth revolved in a circle about the sun.

This theory of Aristarchus was sound enough, given his belief that the sun was a much larger body than the earth. He did not believe that the smaller body could control the movement of the larger one, so he evolved what seemed to him to be a logical theory.

Other scientists at Alexandria's Museum performed equally remarkable work. Eratosthenes, chief librarian of the Museum, made a scientific measurement of the size of the earth. He noted that at the city of Syene the sun was directly overhead at noon on Midsummer Day, while at Alexandria, on the same day, the sun's rays were seven degrees from the vertical, a value estimated from the length of a shadow cast by a vertical rod. Eratosthenes stated that Alexandria was 5,000 stades north of Syene, so the circumference of the earth was 250,000 stades. According to his measurement the diameter of the earth was supposed to be about 7,850 miles, which is accurate within about fifty miles. Eratosthenes was the greatest geographer of his era. He established mathematical geography, which was essential to make any sense of points of reference on an earth that is a sphere.

The major geographic work of Eratosthenes was his *Hypomnemata Geographica,* which was remarkable more for the knowledge of human geography it displayed than for descriptive geography. In other words, he knew where peoples lived and how they lived, but he did not know the shapes of the land masses. This teacher was also an astronomer and a mathematician of some note, and a student of the science of languages—philology. He was a historian, and he wrote a history of philosophy, as well as a partial history of geography, in his *Hypomnemata,* and he was a poet of some note.

Eratosthenes was helped in his conceptions of geography by some remarkable work done by others twenty-five or thirty years before his time. The Phocaean sea captain Pytheas made a great voyage about 300 B.C., at a time when the Phoenicians of Carthage were expanding and trying to keep the entrance to the Atlantic Ocean free from outsiders. Pytheas slipped through the Strait of Gibraltar, eluding the Carthaginians, and sailed north to visit the tin mines of Cornwall, in England, which were then famous in the Mediterranean world. Pytheas was an educated man and an astronomer, so his voyage was far more valuable to science than were many sea voyages of earlier times. He determined the latitude of Marseilles almost exactly, and his observations about other points on the globe gave later geographers accurate information for their work. It was Pytheas who produced the information that allowed Eratosthenes to locate Ireland properly in its relation to England.

One of the mathematical wizards of this period was Apollonius of Perga, who made his calculations at about the same time that Eratosthenes was working on his

geography. Apollonius was a student of the equally tal-
ented and far more famous Archimedes. Perhaps Archimedes should be mentioned first, since he was the elder
of the two and his works undoubtedly influenced Apollonius. Archimedes invented a number of instruments,
including an orrery (a mechanical sphere) to represent
the heavens. He lived in Syracuse, not in Alexandria, but
he spent some time in Egypt. He was a mathematician
who wrote on geometry, algebra, and arithmetic, and he
was a physicist, the creator of two branches of theoretical
mechanics: statics and hydrostatics. He was credited with
inventing, while he was in Egypt, a spiral pump to raise
water from the Nile River. He is supposed to have
launched a great galley for his friend King Hiero in his
Sicilian home city of Syracuse, by using a system of
compound pulleys. One of his famous propositions was the
principle that a body wholly or partly immersed in a fluid
displaced an amount of weight equal to that of the fluid
displaced, a discovery he is supposed to have made in his
bath. He thus became one of the earliest students of what
we know as physics. Another was Euclid, who had studied
geometric optics. But these men, with a handful of later
Alexandrians, stood nearly alone in the world until the
time of Galileo.

Apollonius was some twenty-five years younger than
Archimedes. He was born in Pamphylia, a small country
on the southern coast of Asia Minor, just west of Cyprus.
Because he showed great aptitude as a student, he was
sent to study at the center of learning, Alexandria, where
he remained for the rest of his life. He wrote eight books
on conic sections and devoted a certain amount of his
time to astronomy, during which he invented a system

of epicycles for the movement of heavenly bodies. Nearly two thousand years later Johannes Kepler was to make use of the knowledge of conics supplied by Apollonius and apply it to his studies of the mechanics of the skies.

Archimedes died classically and heroically in 212 B.C. when the Roman general Marcellus laid siege to the city of Syracuse, where Archimedes had long since returned to live. He instructed the defenders of Syracuse in many engineering devices which made the Roman conquest a difficult one. Eventually the Romans breached the wall and rushed into the city. It is said that a Roman soldier came across Archimedes while he was busy staring at some geometric figures he had drawn in the sand, and that when he told the soldier to keep off his drawing the soldier drew his sword and killed the old philosopher.

Apollonius probably died no such heroic death. In fact, there is no record of his death, and only a little is known of his life—as with so many of these ancients, for it was their work that was paramount, not their personal lives.

Ctesibius, an inventor of the period, made a water clock of considerable accuracy, a water organ, a pump, and a compressed air gun. In the time of the second Ptolemy, Alexandrian engineers built the Pharos, a gleaming white marble tower that served as a lighthouse—not to guide ships at night and in fog, but as a point of reference for the mariners who sailed almost always in daylight hours.

In the field of medicine and understanding of the human body the Alexandrians were responsible for important beginnings. One of these was in the study of anatomy. There was no religious prejudice in Alexandria against dissection of the human body, so the scientists at the Museum were able to work freely. Nor did scientists face the problem of justifying themselves to the general public. They acted as teachers to only a few persons, worked under the direct power of the king, and had no reason to fear the superstitious minds of priests or ministers.

One of the leading students of anatomy of the period was Herophilus of Chalcedon, who came to the Museum in the time of the first Emperor Ptolemy. He is supposedly the first Greek to undertake dissection of the human body in public. He is responsible for the naming of many of the parts of the body, since he was the first to describe them. The number of organs he described and investigated is too large to be listed here; he wrote a book of three parts on anatomy, another on the eyes, and still another in which he described proper practices for midwives. Herophilus understood the human circulatory system better than any student before him. Others had known the difference between veins and arteries, but Herophilus described them in detail. He also announced that contrary to older ideas, the arteries were filled with blood—not with air. He also corrected an error by Aristotle, who had believed that the heart was the seat of the intellect. Herophilus returned to the earlier view of Alcmaeon that the brain is the organ of thought.

A young contemporary of Herophilus was Erasistratus, who had studied extensively in Athens before he came to Alexandria. This man made a number of important discoveries about the body and might have discovered the true nature of human blood circulation had he not accepted the idea that the arteries were filled with air. These two students of the body were almost unhampered in their work—and it is said that they even carried out vivisection on animals and human beings, using prisoners turned over to them by the king to observe the functions of organs of the living body.

Other Greek physicians of this period contributed greatly to the understanding of medicine. Praxagoras studied the pulse and used it in the diagnosis of human ills. Herophilus improved on the practice, employing a water clock to measure the pulse rate. Erasistratus was the first Greek physician to discard the theory of humors, such as bile and phlegm, which earlier physicians thought controlled the health of the body. Others in Alexandria studied in different fields. Apollodorus wrote about drugs and poisons, as did Philinos and Andreas. So well known were the Greek physicians at this time in history that many of them were invited to other parts of the world, particularly to Rome, which was rising as Greece fell, and which achieved political power in the Mediterranean as Alexandria, standing nearly alone, guarded the knowledge of the past and carried it forward.

Early Greek ways were not exactly like ours, of course. The Alexandrians wanted a fine library, so they set out to get it by the most direct means possible. The third Ptolemy ordered that all travelers who arrived in Alexandria should give up their books for inspection. If such books were different from those already contained in the Library they were kept, and the traveler was given a specially made copy, transcribed on papyrus. Half a dozen distinguished scholars served as directors of the Library during the 150 years beginning in the third century B.C., during which the Library's great collection was acquired and, to a large extent, classified. These librarians prepared new editions of the works of Homer. They set down the important works of other ancients, and established a chronology of the old Greek world which became invaluable, for before that time each region or locality had its own chronology, so that they often conflicted. Aristophanes of Byzantium, one of the librarians, devised a system of punctuation, similar to the one we now use.

At the time when the Alexandrian Museum was beginning to accomplish much in the field of scientific discovery, science in Babylon continued to prosper, under the Seleucid and Chaldean rulerships. One of the important men in Babylonian science was Berossus, a priest of Marduk, the chief Babylonian god. Berossus was to be more important to the West than to his own country, for he was the figure who brought much of Chaldean and Babylonian astronomy to the Hellenic world.

Berossus lived most of his life in Babylon, but toward the end he moved to the Hellenic island of Cos, where Hippocrates had lived. There Berossus founded a school at which he taught Babylonian science—particularly astronomy and astrology. The rulers of Cos were eager to have that island gain a reputation for culture. The Hellenic leaders of this period showed a high regard for learning, and although every city and every state sought riches, they sought also to increase their prestige by housing men of learning. Thus Berossus was encouraged to write a major work—which he called *Babylonica*. It was divided into three parts. One part dealt with the history of mankind from the Creation until the Great Flood (also part of the Biblical tradition). A second volume dealt with the period from the Flood to the time of Nabonassar—which, Berossus claimed, was a span of 35,000 years. The final book brought the study of Babylonian astronomy and astrology up to nearly "modern" times, from the author's point of view.

This work by a Babylonian became very well known in the Hellenic world and influenced a number of students of cosmology and the stars. The Babylonians had a long tradition of careful scientific observation for their guidance, and this tradition now became a part of the Hellenic world, spreading through Egypt and the eastern Mediterranean. Some of the knowledge of these ancients had come to Greece at the time of Pythagoras, and some in the period in between, but the impact of Babylon came most strongly after the third century B.C., when Babylonian, Egyptian, Greek, and Ionian or other Greek islanders met along the eastern shore of their ocean.

The Babylonian calendar was based on the moon, so the astronomer-priests kept reliable records of its waxing and waning. They used arithmetic instead of geometry to track the heavenly bodies, but there was much the Greeks could learn from them about the techniques of observation. It is important to realize, too, that it was now possible for the Greeks to learn these new methods, because old Babylon was under the domination of another of the military families of the Alexandrian regime. When Egypt had fallen to the Ptolemies in the split-up, Mesopotamia had gone to the Seleucid dynasty, and generally speaking, these two governments were friendly.

Thus Babylon contributed much to Greek astronomy. It also provided the basis for the astrology that developed rapidly in Ptolemaic Egypt and spread to Rome and to northern Europe, where it remained.

Even as the interchanges between the world of Alex-

andria and of Babylon brought astrology, the pseudo
science dealing with the effect of the stars on human affairs,
to the Hellenes, there continued to be progress in the real
sciences. In mathematics, there would be no such golden
age anywhere as that of the third century B.C. for nearly
two thousand years, but men did continue to study mathematics at the Museum, and elsewhere. One of the most
important of these men was Hipparchus of Nicaea, who
founded the study of trigonometry, which was to become
vital in astronomy and celestial navigation.

Hipparchus wrote widely on mathematical problems,
and although his great works have been lost, much of
their value has been retained in the works of later scholars. His system of trigonometry underwent some great
changes before it came down to the present world, but
the basic foundation of that branch of mathematics is
his, and later men modified his work. Hipparchus invented
the basic system of solving spherical triangles and showed
how to deduce the sizes of some of the parts, given other
parts.

Hipparchus was an important astronomer, too. He
worked with epicycles, those mathematical circular systems
which were supposed to account for the movements of
the heavenly bodies. (He also repudiated the idea that
the sun is the center of the solar system—although in
those days there was no differentiation between the solar
system and the universe.) Hipparchus discovered the pre-
cession of the equinoxes, the points of intersection in
spring and fall when the ecliptic and the equator meet
in the celestial sphere. Each year, because of the motion
of the earth on its axis, the equinoxes change a little in
time. They precede the sun slightly, which is why they

Egyptian terra-cotta piece bearing symbols of the zodiac used by Greek scholars in Alexandria

are called precessions, and the slight amount of change is measurable. Hipparchus observed this change a number of times and measured the degree of obliquity of the ecliptic and equator.

Like Aristarchus, Hipparchus tried to measure the distances of both sun and moon from the earth. Also, like Aristarchus, he failed to find the proper distances or sizes of the bodies, but he did again show that the measurements were possible if an accurate method of making them were discovered. Hipparchus also prepared a star calendar, naming some 850 stars, probably deriving some of his figures from Babylonian sources. It is certain that he used some of the old Babylonian calculations and observations in arriving at his own findings. The influence of Babylon was growing in the astronomy of the West. It was to be in large part the basis for Western astronomy for the next sixteen hundred years, for the development of European astronomy came to a standstill in the Greek, or Hellenic, period. After Hipparchus, Posidonius of Apamea and Geminus of Rhodes continued to try to measure the size of the earth, by calculating the distance and difference in latitude between Alexandria and Rhodes. The figure arrived at by Posidonius was wrong, and his mistake was later to create errors in the calculations of Ptolemy, one of the greatest geographers who ever lived.

CHAPTER 8

The End of Alexandria

THE importance of the Museum of Alexandria declined after the middle of the second century before Christ but it never ceased to attract scholars and students as long as it existed and as long as the great hoard of books was kept within its sister institution, the Library. Still, after the second century the power of Rome began to infringe on all the Mediterranean. Julius Caesar captured Alexandria in 48 B.C., and it is said that he burned part of the Library, or at least part of its collection of books. Marc Antony is supposed to have given Cleopatra 200,000 volumes in 41 B.C., from the library of Pergamum, to replace this destruction. But Cleopatra fell, and with her the last vestige of independent rule of Egypt. Rome was all-powerful, and from this time on, except for a handful of students and one genius, little more was to be heard from Alexandria or, for that matter, from the Greeks in terms of the advancement of science. Two men stand out in the later Greek period, almost alone. Ptolemy, the great astronomer and geographer, was one. The other was Galen, the great physician. These two, in a sense, embodied the greatness of Greece, for they prepared encyclopedic volumes of information, some of that information coming from their own contributions, but much of it picked up from the greats of earlier times. These last great Greeks lived in the period of the first and second centuries after the birth of Christ.

In a sense the story of the rise of Rome is the story of the decline of Greek science, although Rome was not dedicated to the destruction of learning—far from it. As the Romans extended their power south and east they gained a great respect for Greek learning and, in fact, used Greek as the language of educated speech and writing. It was only when certain Roman intellectuals broke away in disgust at this dualism and attempted to make Latin the language of the educated that Roman scholars began to write in Latin to any great extent. During this period the Library and the Museum continued to exist, but they were seldom mentioned in Roman studies. After the several burnings of the Greek quarter of the city between the second and sixth centuries A.D., the fate of the books in the Library is obscure. There are many stories about them, but not one that encompasses all the facts.

During the second century before Christ, the city of Alexandria began its decline, for several reasons, in addition to the effects of the movements of the Romans. The Ptolemies were growing weak as the family line moved further away from the great general. Other Hellenistic cities were rising to challenge the business and cultural leadership of Alexander's chosen capital of the world.

Pergamum was to develop a library large enough to attract plunderers because the city was to undergo a period of development in the second and first centuries before Christ—particularly finding leadership in the fields of art and public works. One of Pergamum's remarkable achievements, from the point of view of scientific history, was an elaborate system in which water was carried for many miles across hills and valleys and then piped beneath the city.

In other areas of Hellas, Greeks of East and West led in the development of botany, and of what we would now call pharmacology. They led also in the study of medicine, although until the time of Galen there were no greats in this field, either in Greece or in the surrounding lands.

Crates of Mallus, the director of the Pergamese library, was a student of languages of some note during the next to last century before Christ and made some contribution to the study of geography. Strabo, the great geographer born in 64 B.C., wrote one of the most famous geographies of all time. He traveled from Armenia to Egypt, to Greece, to Italy, and he sailed up the Nile as far as Ethiopia. He studied in Rome and in Alexandria, which made of him a sort of bridge between the two cultures—Greek and Roman—during a critical period in history. The value of Strabo's work, basically, is as an encyclopedia of the geographic knowledge of that time, for his books have come down to us relatively intact, whereas others, perhaps more valuable, have been lost. Strabo's is not mathematical geography, but human geography. He was interested in the peoples of the world and their surroundings. He never made a real effort to try to place the physical features of the world in a systematic fashion, but he showed a considerable knowledge of natural history, and of the phenomena of nature, such as earthquakes, volcanoes, and erosion.

Historians end the Hellenic age with the appearance of the Christian religion in the world, which means that the last two great Greeks do not properly belong to the Hellenic age in terms of time. Before they made their belated appearance on the scene of science, what had been accomplished by the Greeks? So much, says Professor George Sarton in his *History of Science,* that with all the discoveries of the modern world, it cannot be said that Western civilization has done so much in the three centuries since the coming of the *Mayflower* to the shores of North America. Scientific research was organized as never before in the Museum at Alexandria. Large libraries were established at Alexandria and Pergamum—and later they were robbed to form a great library at Rome. The period saw the rise of mathematics to a degree unequaled for another seventeen hundred years. A number of astronomers, Greek and Chaldean, made amazing discoveries. Students of the world made discoveries in physics, they built engineering marvels, they developed scientific agriculture, they created systems of anatomy and physiology, studied geography and history, invented a system of Greek grammar, and began the study of scientific philology. Theirs was a great period.

Before going on to the post-Hellenic period, one warning seems to be in order and that is against oversimplification. We do not really know very much about the ancients. Our knowledge is fragmentary, parts of it come from translations of translations, parts come from parts of books and poems, inscriptions, and ancient objects. At times an object turns up which throws an entirely new light on some phase of ancient knowledge.

For example, within the past few years skin divers, searching for treasure off the Greek islands, discovered corroded fragments of some kind of mechanism in the remains of a sunken Greek ship off the island of Antikythera. Derek J. de Solla Price, a historian of science who had studied ancient scientific instruments, assembled the fragments and after examining them decided that they were parts of an astronomical computer of a most advanced type, dating from 82 B.C. and used for the study of complex cycles in the movement of heavenly bodies. Here was an example of a technology that existed in the Hellenic world, one so complicated that we must have the highest respect for it, and one about which little was known before Dr. Price made his studies. And it must be assumed that there is a great deal about the ancients that is yet unknown, much of it of a surprising nature. In the past there has been far too much underestimation of the ancients.

Of the last two Greek greats who followed this period, the first was Ptolemy (or Claudius Ptolemaeus, to give him his Romanized name, since he lived in an Alexandria that was a Roman colony). The life of Ptolemy is a mystery to us. It is known that he lived in Alexandria between 127 and 157 A.D. and that he made observations of the skies there during that period. But his observations were not as accurate as those of Hipparchus who preceded him. Indeed, Ptolemy drew heavily on Hipparchus in his writings about the skies, and Hipparchus might be placed among the greatest astronomers of all times, along with Ptolemy.

The Ptolemaic system of the universe is a complicated study in itself and demands a knowledge of higher mathematics, which Ptolemy had. The Ptolemaic theory has been compared with Einstein's Theory of Relativity in one sense; the average Greek did not understand the Ptolemaic theory any more readily than the average American understands the Einstein theory nearly two thousand years later.

The importance of Ptolemy's theory was that it gave a logical, mathematical explanation of the movement of the heavenly bodies. In a sense, Ptolemy was a synthesist. He adopted the fundamental assertions of the astronomy of Hipparchus and improved upon them. He believed that the heavens made up a sphere which turned around a fixed axis, and that the earth too is a sphere, placed in the center of the heavens. He did not believe that the earth could turn on its axis, else men and heavy objects

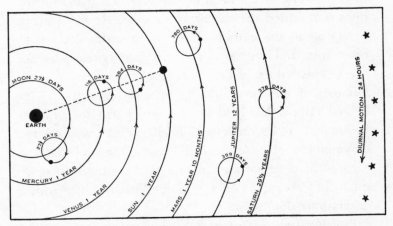

COURTESY OF THE AMERICAN MUSEUM OF NATURAL HISTORY

The Ptolemaic System

would be thrown into the air from the earth, but he noted that if earth should indeed turn on its axis, astronomical theory would be simplified a great deal.

Ptolemy used the system of eccentric circles and epicycles which had been used by Hipparchus. He also added to them. He advanced new ideas about the moon and the planets, although he accepted most of Hipparchus' ideas about the sun. J. L. E. Dreyer, one of the early historians of astronomy in this century, has noted that Ptolemy's system as a whole deserves the admiration of the twentieth century, although it was not the system that we have accepted, nor was it correct in its basic premise that the earth was the center of the universe. What Ptolemy's system did do was to present geometrically the movements of the planets, as accurately as the instruments then in use could be made to follow them. It required some eighty circles to explain such movements of the heavens in this theory, and it must not be supposed that Ptolemy himself regarded the theory as absolute. He made a discovery about the motion of the moon which did not fit his theory and suggested that his own system was not exact. The failure of the time, and it was not Ptolemy's but that of the times, was the lack of regard that both he and Hipparchus held for the theory that the sun was the center of the universe. These two men stopped the development of other theories except the one that the earth is the center of the universe until the time of Copernicus. But *they* did not stop it—the blind faith of future generations stopped it.

Ptolemy was important for many other reasons. His great work has come down to us as a translation from the Greek, probably into Syriac or another Eastern lan-

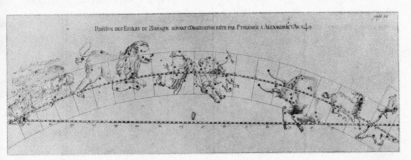

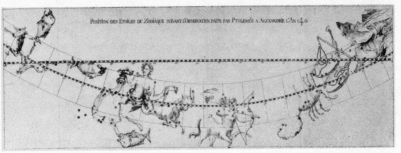

The twelve zodiacal constellations as described by Ptolemy

guage, then into Arabic, then into Latin, and finally into the modern Western languages. It is called commonly by its Arabic name, the *Almagest*. It is a combination of history of astronomy of the ancients, a study of the system of the universe that Ptolemy had advanced, and a system of star charts, most of which he had inherited from Hipparchus, who apparently got some of them from the ancient Babylonians and the later Chaldeans. Ptolemy gives us all the information we have about certain ancient mathematicians and students of astronomy. His judgments of these men and their work are the only ones available in some cases, since the original work of the men, and of their critics and students, have all been lost.

Ptolemy was also important to science as a geographer. He produced the last important geographical study in the days of the Hellenes. No such work was again undertaken for a very long time. Hipparchus had been a geographer and had suggested that someone ought to determine the points of latitude and longitude of the important spots of the world—cities and coastal points—for the purpose of guiding mapmakers in making accurate maps of the known world. That idea of Hipparchus was certainly a scientific approach to geography. A geographer named Marinus of Tyre undertook just such a task around 150 A.D., but he did not complete the work. Ptolemy later took over and did advance it as far as he was able, writing eight books dedicated to the subject of geography. Six of those books are lists of places and their latitude and longitude, but most of the locations are estimates. None of his longitudes were determined astronomically, nor were many of his latitudes. Ptolemy also picked up the erroneous figure given by Posidonius for the circumference of the earth, rather than the more correct one discovered earlier by Eratosthenes. For that reason most of his distances were exaggerated. Historians of science have remarked on the significance of this error: more than thirteen hundred years later it was to lead Christopher Columbus to try to reach Asia by sailing west, because the maps he studied, based even then on the Ptolemaic projections, showed Asia and Europe far closer together than they actually are. Ptolemy was a good student of his subject, and his Hellenic contemporaries were learning ever more about the world around them. In the time of Eratosthenes, the Greeks knew only of lands that extended as far east as the Ganges. At least they knew those lands well enough to map them. But Ptolemy knew of the existence of the Malay Peninsula and of China.

The work of the second great man of the last years of Hellenic science was done in Pergamum, at Alexandria, and at Rome, where so many of the fine manuscripts of the Greek world had been moved in the course of the Roman conquests of the Mediterranean world. The man was Galen, known as Claudius Galen in Rome. Even before his birth in 138 A.D. the Romans had shown how poorly they regarded the arts of medicine by refusing for the most part to engage in them. Arturo Castiglioni notes that by the end of the Roman Republic the physicians in Rome were nearly all foreigners, and perhaps this distaste of the Romans for an aspect of science that the Greeks held in high respect shows why the Greeks and not the Romans were the leaders in scientific thought.

Even before Galen, the Greek physicians were regarded as the finest in the Western world. They made no distinction between medicine and surgery; it was all a matter of performing operations and selling medicines. They were soon employed by the patrician families of Rome. Next they became the physicians of gladiators, and then of all Rome. Many of these Greek physicians were slaves; some of them were freed by their masters for saving their lives. During the last years of the Roman Republic, the privileges of citizenship were often granted to Greek physicians who came to live in Rome. Asclepiades of Prusa, sometimes called the prince of physicians, was a friend of Marc Antony. This physician studied in the medical school in Alexandria and became one of the best known in all Rome. He was able to diagnose malaria accurately, he was a student of mental diseases, and he prescribed diet, exercise, massage, and hydrotherapy for his patients.

This story of the rise to fame of Asclepiades has been told by the Roman Lucius Apuleius, and although historians of science do not accept it as being true, it does indicate the manner in which certain physicians gained fame in Rome:

Asclepiades had come to Rome and earned a certain fame by his treatments, but he was not much better known than many other Greek physicians of the period. One day, on the way to his villa, Asclepiades encountered a funeral procession on the Via Sacra. A large number of Romans were walking along the road, weeping in the fashion of the day, and in the middle of the procession came the coffin bearers, carrying the corpse. They tired from the exertion and sat down to rest, while the Greek physician stopped and asked members of the funeral what had caused the death of the person they were about to bury. No one could answer properly, so Asclepiades looked closely at the corpse and thought he saw traces of life. He extinguished the funeral flame, already lit, and told the dead one's friends and relatives to stop preparations for the funeral banquet. He had members of the funeral procession carry the body into a neighboring house, and he went inside after them. For several minutes he manipulated the supposed corpse, and those inside were astonished to see the dead return to life. The news of this miraculous cure spread through Rome that very day, and Asclepiades' fortune and fame were assured.

In a way, Hippocratic medicine, the highest type up

to that time, was being corrupted in Rome. After Asclepiades came the school of medicine represented by those
known as Methodists, a group supposedly founded by
Themison. Some Romans joked that Themison killed so
many patients they could not be counted. He is given
credit (or blame) for drawing medicine into rigid doctrines. He said that diseases are divided into two fundamental kinds, one representing a state of tension and the
other a state of relaxation, and that both were dependent
on the state of the pores of the body. His medical treatment was simple enough. It consisted of following two
sets of remedies, designed either to combat tension or to
combat relaxation. The common people of Rome liked
this system because they could understand it, or they
thought they could, although the Methodists did not discuss its principles with their patients.

In the time of the Roman Empire, the tradition of the
upper class forbade patricians to practice medicine, making it possible for the Greeks almost to monopolize the
field. In this period, Roman medicine was for all practical purposes Greek medicine, and the Romans confined
themselves more or less to writing about medical practice, which a number of them did with great skill.

In addition, several other schools of medicine flourished
in and around Rome. By the middle of the first century
of the Christian Era, however, it was apparent that there
was no real progress being made in scientific concept of
medicine, and that the works of Hippocrates were being
denuded of their meaning. Then, Claudius Galen appeared on the scene.

Galen studied first, apparently, at the famous temple
of Asclepius in his home at Pergamum. He pursued phi-

losophy as a youth. Later he turned to medicine and studied anatomy and the actual care of patients, under two well-known teachers, Satyrus and Stratonicus, at Pergamum. He studied next at Smyrna under a famous physician and then went to the medical school at Alexandria for a concentrated period of exposure to the advanced anatomy courses offered there to the lucky few. Ten years after he left Pergamum he returned to that city. He was then just twenty-eight years old but already among the best known of the Hellenic physicians.

Galen was appointed physician to the gladiators of Pergamum and gained considerably more fame in this post. A few years later he decided to move to Rome. Within months he was the leading physician in all Rome, treating patients, both rich and poor, and lecturing and experimenting on animals in the public theaters. He was one of the most productive of writers among the ancient medical men, and also one of the most unpopular because of his great success and his lack of shyness in broadcasting it.

Through many long years of practice, Galen never stopped his writing. Before he died he had composed some four hundred separate works. Most of these were lost, but a hundred or more of them have been retained, either in Latin or in Arabic translations. He wrote on the attributes of the ideal physician, on philosophy, on anatomy, on the blood vessels, physiology, and many other subjects. The work of Galen marks an end to a period in the history of medicine. His work is that of a gifted man of medicine, but on the other side it shows the dogmatism of a man convinced of his infallibility, and one who relied on an Aristotelian philosophy to lay down dogma—always injurious to science.

Galen thought he knew everything and could cure every ill; he did know more about the anatomy of animals than any man previous to this time.

Philosophically, Galen took the position that the body was only an instrument of the soul. In some ways he was responsible for the perpetuation of many fundamental errors that worked to delay the progress of medicine— here again it was not so much the fault of Galen as the undue acceptance of his dogmatic statements by people who lived long after him. Many of his ideas lived through the days of ancient medicine in the West and until the Renaissance.

Galen understood the brain as had none before. He knew that the arteries contained blood, not air, but he did not understand the circulatory system. He demonstrated the relationship between nerves and muscles, showing how paralysis of muscles followed the cutting of certain nerves, and he showed how the brain was the nervous center of the body, not the heart as had been earlier believed. Galen also arrived at a basic principle of modern medicine: that every change in function in an organ is caused by an injury to the organ, and that every injury to an organ results in a change in function.

Once a Persian philosopher in Rome suffered a sensory paralysis, or loss of feeling, in the fourth and fifth fingers of one hand. He called in physicians of the Methodist school, who first applied medicines to the fingers. None of them helped, so he called in Galen.

Galen asked first if the Persian had hurt his arm. The

philosopher replied that he had fallen on a sharp stone and had received a blow between the shoulders. He had felt pain at the time but this had gone away.

Galen diagnosed the man's problem as an inflammation of the spinal cord. He ordered the patient to bed, and told his nurses to apply soothing remedies to the Persian's upper back. The patient recovered the use of his fingers. Galen explained that he knew the problem arose in the area of the seventh cervical vertebra. He knew that every nerve has an origin quite apart from other nerves, but that they unite, while maintaining their individual characteristics. He also knew that the nerve which controlled those fingers began at the seventh vertebra. Later, he told other physicians why there was a paralysis of feeling although the Persian could still move his fingers—it was, he explained, because muscles and skin were controlled by separate nerves, and that only the muscles of the skin were affected in this case.

Obviously Galen had much to teach the practitioners of medicine if they had known how to separate the real from the unreal in his philosophy and teachings. But his genius was, in a sense, a victim of the times. Those who came after him seemed to lack the same critical faculties he had exercised in accepting some of the ideas of others and rejecting some. It was the end of the period of Greek discovery, and that period gave way to acceptance of dogmas, and to the criticism of criticism.

There was nothing very sudden about the decline of the scientific spirit in the Roman world, or in the world of the Greeks who were being swallowed by the Romans. Greek or Hellenic civilization had lost its impetus in the fragmentation of the empire after Alexander's time. Here and there, as in Alexandria, conditions arose which brought about the concentration of fertile minds for a time. Once the Museum and Library were established and their fame was made known to the Hellenic world, it was easy enough for a tolerant Ptolemy to attract the prime thinkers of his period. His son did the same, but thereafter the Ptolemies turned their minds to other subjects, to military conquest on a small scale, to luxury, and, in general, away from the pursuit of knowledge for its own sake.

The rate of advance in Greek science had slowed down appreciably by the middle of the second century before Christ. Four centuries later, after Galen, progress had ended altogether, and indeed the tendency was for men to backtrack from scientific ways of doing things.

The interesting new idea advanced by the Greeks in terms of the study of the world—and this included the skies—was their assumption that the whole of the universe *could* be understood by men, in terms of their own experience. This was an entirely new approach to life, and if it was an oversimplification (which we of a more scientific society understand it to be), still it was better to oversimplify, and try, than to treat the world as a grand mystery and cover up facts with mumbo-jumbo.

Aristotle recognized two elements of existence, matter and form. To him the object of science was the knowledge of forms. This idea served the Greeks well in the study of plants and animals, and with it the biological sciences made great strides.

The idea of form, however, did not help much in the sphere of physics. Form was useful in terms of those units or individuals which showed growth cycles. What was needed for the advancement of physics was a concept of *forces,* which neither Aristotle's biology nor the mathematics of the Greeks provided. What was needed was a different way of thinking, particularly by those who might observe, and experiment.

Mathematics advanced further with the Greeks than did any other branch of science, but up to the third century before Christ all science had advanced so rapidly that it became an instrument of power through prestige. Thus was established the Museum of Alexandria and similar institutions.

Greek science was not killed. It died because it had advanced to the limit of possible expansion within its mold. Historians attribute some of the failures of the Greek and Roman civilization to the existence of slavery, and cheap labor, and an aversion to manual labor (or in the case of the Roman patricians, contact with the masses) by the free men of the world. Part of the blame for failure has been placed at the feet of the Christian church by certain historians of science, but that failure did not come in the time of the Greek scientists. On the basis of military conquest and leadership, even political leadership, the Romans should have displaced the Greeks as the leaders of science well before the beginning of the Christian Era. Instead, the Romans contributed very little to science, and the study of the Roman period, after the decline of the Museum of Alexandria, is the study of the stagnation of science in the West.

CHAPTER 9

Science and Decline Under the Romans

ROME was founded in the eighth century before Christ and grew steadily, like a strong if badly behaved child who fought with everyone in sight and usually succeeded in winning, or, failing to win, came back later to win another day. But Roman and Hellenic affairs did not mingle seriously until around 212 B.C., when Rome was called into the affairs of Rhodes and Pergamum to arbitrate differences with other Hellenic states.

Little by little Rome swallowed the fragments of Alexander's empire. In one hundred years the generals and their descendants had learned very little about the strength of union and the weakness of tiny independent kingdoms, and nearly at the beginning of the second century before Christ, the Aetolian and Achaean leagues were swallowed up. In 148 B.C., Macedonia, home of Philip and Alexander, the conquerors, became a Roman province. In 146 B.C., after Carthage was destroyed and Rome had no vigorous opponent in all the Mediterranean, the Romans suddenly relaxed, and began an active appreciation of Greek culture.

When Julius Caesar appeared on the Roman scene as a power—during the Gallic wars of 58–51 B.C.—the Romans had already adopted the trappings of Greek culture and had accepted the Greek philosophy of the superiority of mental genius over power. And yet the Romans did not ever adopt the Greek way of looking at life— quizzically, with an egocentric self-assurance that all problems in the universe could be solved. The Romans were egotistical enough, but not quite in the same way as the Greeks were.

Caesar was a man of letters—he introduced the Egyptian calendar into Rome and thus assured its journey down through the centuries in the hands of the Christian church. But other Romans contented themselves with understanding what the Greeks had done and not why they had done it. In the middle of the last century before the birth of Christ the great Cicero noted that Greek mathematicians led the field in geometry while Romans contented themselves with reckoning and measuring. Generally speaking, that was the Roman attitude toward science.

The great schools at Athens continued, but they did not prosper. Stoicism became the most popular philosophy and religion of the time, and while there was much that was good in their ideas that virtue is based on knowledge and that the good man lives in harmony with nature, the urge to study nature seemed to diminish, and at the same time the Stoics began to lean to astrology. They believed that the universe is an organic, whole entity, with each part dependent on the others. They were fatalists; they felt that man's actions from birth to death were preordained. They could discover the ways of providence by divination—by reading special signs in the stars and in other ways.

When one speaks of science in Rome, the name of Titus Lucretius Carus is always mentioned, for he wrote a book whose title indicates that it was a study of all nature: *De rerum natura (On the Nature of Things)*. The book was written well before his death in 55 B.C. and apparently was preserved because it came to the favorable attention of the powerful Cicero.

Lucretius' book was a defense of the Epicurean philosophy. It was an encyclopedia which showed how the Romans felt about the philosophical studies of the ancient Greeks, and what attitude Romans took toward science and many other parts of Greek culture. That is why the book is so important—not because it indicated any original thinking on the part of Lucretius in the matters of science. He was trying to explain nature on the basis of facts. He feared both superstition and religion as enemies of philosophical and scientific study.

And what of Roman study of the stars?

A leading student of the heavens was Publius Nigidius Figulus, also a friend of Cicero, who was himself deeply interested in astronomy. Nigidius Figulus was one of the Stoics who sought answers to the secrets of life from the stars. He was the first to give Latin names to the constellations and the stars, but he later turned to astrology, believing it to be a proper application of the mechanics of astronomy. He cast a horoscope for Octavius (who became the Emperor Augustus) and predicted that he would become master of the world.

Another student of the period who was important in Roman affairs was Marcus Terentius Varro. This man, once soldier and statesman, began his intellectual studies at the age of seventy-three and continued until he died at ninety. He, too, was an encyclopedist, one who produced seven major works during those last sixteen years of his life, on subjects as different as rhetoric and mathematics. He taught in Latin, rather than Greek, and he helped bring astrology to Rome as a powerful force in politics and social life.

Hyginus, a slave who later was in charge of the Palatine library, wrote widely on astronomy and seems to have been one of the best-educated men in Rome on that subject. But most Romans turned to the new astrology.

This astrology began when someone, perhaps in the Greek world, came to the conclusion that each man's personal fate could be deduced by examining the relative positions of the planets and major stars at the time of his birth, and then interpreting them according to rules laid down by trial and error—or by study of the lives of a number of others.

The first known horoscopes were recorded on cuneiform tablets but they were rare. The art of astrology was not finely developed in Babylon, but in Egypt, during the Alexandrian period, and especially at the end of the truly scientific period when Roman rule was spreading across the Greek world. Astrology seems to have been a creation by Greek-Egyptians, using materials from Ancient Egypt and Ancient Babylon.

The practice of making and selling horoscopes became so popular in Rome that it was outlawed in 139 B.C. by the Roman Senate, because so many quacks were preying on the Roman citizenry. The dangers came not from astrology but from the uses to which it was put by the unscrupulous. Astrologers were like magicians, and the wistful and the angry came to them, seeking ways to make loved ones love them in turn, or to revenge themselves on enemies. In spite of its having been banned, the underworld in Rome organized astrology as a racket and it continued, long past the days of the power of Rome, past Rome's fall, through the Dark Ages, the Renaissance, and the Industrial Revolution. Even today at almost any newsstand one may buy an astrological magazine or horoscope, and most newspapers carry daily astrological forecast columns which are among the better-read parts of the newspaper. Largely because of astrology the seven-day week was accepted all over the Western world, as was the twenty-four-hour day, which we have inherited from the Egyptians and the Babylonians. The day of twenty-four equal hours was accepted by believers in astrology long before it was adopted generally, and in some areas of Europe the division of the day into unequal hours (depending on the length of time the sun was in view) continued until as late as the eighteenth century.

If the Romans showed little interest in the spirit of science, and not much progress in the scientific attitude (except in one or two directions), one still cannot write off Roman civilization as a cipher in the story of the growth of science—if for no other reason than the Roman preoccupation with many branches of technology.

The outstanding technical book of the ancient world was written by a Roman in Latin. The Roman was Vitruvius and the book was *De architectura*. It is divided into ten sections dealing with architectural principles, the history of architecture, use of materials, Ionic temples, Doric and Corinthian temples, public buildings, theaters, baths, harbors, houses, interior decoration, water supply, dials and clocks, and mechanical engineering. It was yet another example of the Roman aptitude for writing encyclopedias, but there was also much of value in this encyclopedia. Vitruvius described sound as the displacement of air in waves and then applied that theory to the planning of acoustical properties in buildings. His work, although that of an engineer, also represented a high type of technology involving the use of many mechanical principles which would later fall within the science of physics. One of the great values of the work of Vitruvius is that it was written largely on the basis of firsthand knowledge and thus gave later students an accurate view of the manner in which Roman technicians worked.

The Romans were noted, and justly so, for their public works. They built temples, theaters, monuments, arches, stadiums, bridges, aqueducts, and great public buildings. They installed a drainage system in the Pontine marsh south of Rome to dry it up. This area remained habitable until Rome decayed and fell, after which new swamps were formed by water seepage and it was abandoned because of the constant danger of malaria. The Roman aqueducts were so long and so well built that they remained marvels in the eyes of barbarians and other visitors long after the last noble Roman had passed away. From a point eight miles outside Rome, Agrippa ordered the building of one aqueduct to supply the public baths of the city. When it was finished it was fourteen miles in length. Later the Emperor Augustus built an aqueduct twenty-five miles long, for the sole purpose of providing water for an area in which were staged mimic sea battles.

Caesar's armies crossed the Rhine River on wooden

bridges erected in ten days by his engineers. Other engineers built roads that lasted for centuries. They also built canals, harbors, docks, sewers, and tunnels. These and others were great accomplishments by highly civilized men.

Among the Romans nature was treated as it had never been treated before in art. The Romans were cynically called farmer-warriors. They loved nature, and this love showed in the writings of such as Pliny. Pliny was born at Como in 23 A.D. and studied under several illustrious teachers. He learned botany in Rome, and although he became a soldier, administrator, and lawyer, he did not lose his love for nature. His work *Naturalis Historia* was the greatest of all the encyclopedic works of the Romans devoted to nature. It had all the faults of any encyclopedia, but it had also the great virtue of showing the range of Roman knowledge. Pliny used two thousand different works by some five hundred authors. Most of those original works have disappeared, and were it not for Pliny's distillation of them, there would be no record of much of the knowledge in the field of nature in that time. Pliny may have had no critical faculty, but he covered a great area in eight books: cosmology, geography, anthropology, zoology, botany, medicine, mineralogy, and art.

It is remarkable that in the civilization of Rome no native Roman became a leader in the medical profession, although in a way Rome did encourage the medical arts and medical science. Around the time of the end of the reign of Augustus the societies of doctors built a meeting place in Rome, which they called the medical school. It had both a president and a secretary, and the students of medicine and practitioners met there to discuss tech-

Pliny the Younger

niques and problems. In the time of the Emperor Vespasian, in the second half of the first century of the Christian Era, medical teachers were paid by the government, and the government built halls for the teaching of medicine.

Rome did not produce a great physician but it did produce one great writer on medical matters, Celsus, who wrote *De re medica,* about 30 A.D. Modern scholars suspect that this book is a part of a lost encyclopedia of all ancient medical knowledge, and that it is a translation of some earlier Greek's work, although it was written in Latin and not described as being of Greek origin. The most valuable and instructive part of the book is that dealing with surgical matters. Celsus described plastic

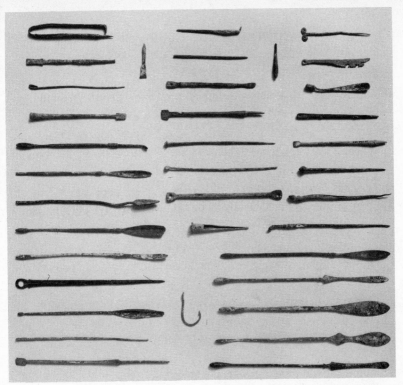

Ancient bronze surgical instruments, implements and utensils found in Rome

surgery, operation for goiter, operation for stones, and what seems to be a tonsilectomy. He also wrote about dentistry, including the wiring of loose teeth by Roman physicians, a practice that is continued by dentists today.

The Romans made complex medical instruments, including forceps, scissors, tweezers, and scalpels, but they did not produce many men of a caliber as high as their implements. Scribonius Largus, physician to the Emperor Claudius and to the Empress Messalina, classified diseases by an ancient Egyptian method of starting with the head and working down to the feet, paying no attention to the organs of the body.

The Romans also knew something about veterinary medicine. They could tell the age of a horse by his teeth and understood such diseases as scabies in sheep, anthrax, rabies, and a number of diseases of cattle. But the great contribution of the Romans to medical science was in public health and hospitalization. From very early times the Romans understood many of the dangers of city life in which people are crammed close together and thus are able to transmit their diseases. In 450 B.C. Rome outlawed burials within the city's walls. Other laws provided for maintenance of the cleanliness of the streets and the sanitary distribution of water from public fountains. In time, the aqueducts built by the engineers totaled fourteen, and they provided three hundred million gallons of water a day for city use, as much as any city provides today on a basis of comparative populations.

Rome's finest contribution came from its preoccupation with the arts of war and conquest. The Roman military system was made up of some twenty-five legions. Each legion contained ten cohorts, and perhaps 7,000 men served in a cohort. To each cohort was assigned a physician. Every ship in the fleet had its own physician. The troops assigned to serve as police and firemen each had their own unit physician. Julius Caesar, noting the importance of physicians, granted citizenship to any doctor who would practice in Rome, in order to attract physicians to the city. These military physicians were given freedom from combat duty and guard duty and were ranked as officers, although most of them were equal to noncommissioned officers in other respects.

Doctors and Roman generals combined their talents to produce a hospital system. In the beginning of Roman conquest, soldiers who fell ill or who were incapacitated by wounds were sent home to recover. But as the legions of Rome moved north, south, east and west it became impossible for soldiers to return to their homes from the far frontiers. For this reason military hospitals were organized. The first of these which has been discovered is a hospital—about twenty miles from Vienna at Carnuntum —which was built in the first century of the Christian Era. Another hospital was built on the lower Rhine, near Düsseldorf. It was arranged as a system of corridors. The entrance was placed between two administrative offices, and inside was a vestibule, off which the corridors and wards stretched around the building. In the center of the building was located the dining hall, and at one end was an advanced system of sanitation.

Such hospitals, called *valetudinaria,* were adopted for the civil population too, first to treat the many Roman officials and families who were sent to the far points of the empire, and eventually to treat the whole population, as the Romans came to realize the benefits of public health.

Among the Romans there were few serious students of mathematical geography, although practical geography, for the measurement of the empire, was carried out carefully. Caesar planned the first survey. It was outlined by M. Vipsanius Agrippa and carried out in 20 B.C., after thirty years of study. The empire's roads were marked out with stones like milestones. Each province had its own surveyors whose reports were available at the provincial governor's offices. From these was prepared a huge map which showed the routes for armies. Besides this large survey, the Romans had maps showing all the roads of the empire.

These were practical matters, to which the Romans were always ready to give attention. They were less interrested in the concept of the entire world or of the universe. Interest in the far reaches of the empire waned in proportion to their distances from Rome. Only one Roman writer, Pomponius Mela, dealt seriously with both general geography and the heavens. His ideas did not add much to the knowledge of the ancient world, but they are important because they were transmitted through the Dark Ages and became the general view of the world at that time.

Pomponius Mela's world was a sphere, with the land surrounded totally by water. The earth was divided into five zones. The middle zone was burned up by the sun and was uninhabitable, as were the two extremes, because of ice. Between the torrid and frigid zones lay the two temperate zones. The Romans lived in one of them on one side of the earth. The half of the world the Romans knew was also supposed to be completely surrounded by water, forming a mass whose lands and continents were separated by smaller bodies of water. The other side of the earth, which the Romans cared little about, was represented as an oblong mass.

Mela's picture of the world was not greatly different from that of the Greek Eratosthenes, but in general the Romans did know a great deal more about northern Europe—and yet it is an indication of their nonscientific approach that they knew so very little, given the opportunity they had to learn so much. They believed, for example, that Spain lay west of Britain, and they were very hazy about Britain's major geographical features as late as the first half of the first century A.D. Ptolemy's studies at that same time were far more complete and it is doubtful that he had the same access to information that a Roman writer might have had—if the Romans had shown any real interest in geography for its own sake.

Pliny raised an issue that was to bother Western man for a long time after the days of the Romans. Scientific geographers took the position that the other side of the world, which they had never seen, was inhabited by Antichthones, people whose feet, when they stood on solid ground, pointed up at the Romans from underneath, while their heads pointed down to the heavens. This, of course, was a recognition of the spherical nature of the earth. But the common people scoffed at the theory. How did the people who lived in the antipodes, or on the other side of the earth, manage to keep from falling off? (As Pliny noted, nobody in Rome seemed to be bothered by the fact that the Romans weren't falling off.) Pliny had no doubt about the roundness of the earth. He knew why he first saw a ship's mast, then the hull, as it approached the shore. But the commoners would have none of it. This had little to do with the progress of science, because the commoners had no control over scientific study, but it did begin to explain how, in the absence of organized scientific activity in the next several hundred years in western Europe, the belief that the earth was flat could gain general acceptance in many places, and by at least some political leaders, who helped perpetuate it among the people.

In about the second century of the Christian Era a

new study became important in Alexandria. This was alchemy, a refinement of the old crafts of working with chemical substances such as dyes and glazes. In previous days, the crafts were associated with magic. Greek potters wore masks to frighten the demons away from their furnaces, lest the demons crack their pottery. The production of metals from ore was regarded as a birth process. Some chemistry was practiced without mumbo-jumbo, as in the preparation of dyes, but far greater rewards were promised to those who might discover the secrets of alchemy.

Alchemy as an art was aimed at the conversion of base metals into gold, and the preparation of a magical mixture that would prolong human life indefinitely. The name alchemy comes from the Arabic *al-kīmīa*. The Arabs were later to expend great efforts in this regard, but their work and later that of European alchemists was preceded by that of the Alexandrians and Romans.

The basic belief was that metals such as copper, tin, lead, and iron were only impure forms of a single metal substance. The pure form was gold. Thus if a base metal could be purified it would be gold. That idea soon became mixed up with a theory that a similar change could be made in man, and that he could be given power to understand and perhaps master the universe.

The alchemists were never to find the secret of everlasting life, but they were to discover some helpful combinations of chemicals and medicines in their laboratories. In that sense, alchemy was not a scientific failure, although the approach to it was anything but scientific.

A common practice of the alchemists was to make an alloy of copper, tin, lead, and iron. The alloy was then whitened with arsenic or mercury vapor, which supposedly gave it the spirit of silver. Next a bit of gold was added, as a baker adds yeast to dough, in order to make the whole mixture expand. Finally, the metal was treated to give it a golden surface, after which some alchemists falsely claimed that they had actually manufactured gold.

Along with the theories of alchemy, astrology, magic, and Stoicism, which tended to destroy the interest of men in the factual approach to life, came the rise of the Christian religion in Rome and the splitting of the Roman Empire into two segments with the removal of the Eastern capital to Byzantium or Constantinople. Christianity did not force science into decline, but it did cause Christians to tend to forget the daily world in their preparation for the heaven of tomorrow. That turn of mind, together with the belief in a number of mysteries, served to push scientific thought into the background. With the rise of Christianity came a regression to the old belief that the earth was flat. The flat-earth theory was accepted by the Syrian Christians in particular.

In the Western world the general idea of the roundness of the earth was preserved, even when Rome fell. But if the earth was round, to discuss it and its place in the heavens did not bring salvation to a Christian, and this was the most important matter in life. At the end of the fourth century A.D., science was in rout in the Western world and the power and glory of Rome and the Greek way of life were forgotten.

In the East, although the Syrians held to their stubborn views, science did not decline as rapidly as in the West. Perhaps it roots were deeper, dating back to those Ionians of the Turkish coastal region. In Athens the Academy and the Lyceum were kept alive until 529 when Justinian ordered them shut down. In this atmosphere of prolonged academic freedom, the students of Athens combined the mathematical ideas of Ptolemy and the cosmology of Aristotle to bring forth a world view which made of Ptolemy's system a physical plan. The heavens were supposed to consist of nine concentric spheres, with the earth in the center, the moon in the first sphere, and the eighth carrying the fixed stars, the ninth being the primum mobile or prime substance. This was really much like the old theories, but Christians were able to accept this view by deciding the movers of the heavenly bodies were seraphs, cherubs, archangels, and angels, with God alone in a tenth heaven.

John Philoponus, a sixth-century student of Alexandria, said that the physical nature of such a universe was not possible—for which he was outlawed as a heretic. Philoponus had suggested that the constant attention of angels and cherubs was not essential. All God needed to have done, he said, was to give a gentle shove in the beginning to start the universe. It could continue by itself, with an impetus supplied by some kind of unseen force.

Aristotle claimed that there could be no such force, and that a vacuum could not exist, for he felt that it was possible to transmit energy only through one substance to another by direct contact. And Aristotle was the lawgiver concerning all physical matters. When he was discovered by the Christians of later times he was embraced by them and for many years men did not successfully contradict anything Aristotle had held to be true. This was the low state to which the spirit of inquiry had fallen in the Western world.

CHAPTER **10**

Science and the Arabs of the East

Between Egypt on the west and Babylonia on the east lay a broad peninsula so largely given over to desert that none of the great conquerors had considered it worth their attention. Although Babylonian, Egyptian, Persian, and Greek had conquered this wedge of Arabia, throughout the centuries there was little noticeable change in the way of life of the Arabs because of it.

The first known mention of an Arab in history is an inscription by the Assyrian Shalmaneser III, who destroyed the capital of the King of Damascus in 854 B.C. and noted that among his booty were a thousand camels of Gindibu, the Arabian. Even then the camel was the symbol of the Arab, because the Arabs were primarily traders. In the north the Arabs moved across the land in caravans. In the south existed a prosperous civilization that linked India with Africa through voyages on the Red Sea and the Indian Ocean. The area was subjugated by Rome, which held its cities and robbed its traders, but the way of life was not seriously changed. Indeed, Rome brought assets to the Arabs, for Arab fighting men became auxiliaries to the Roman legions.

At the end of the sixth century of the Christian period, Rome had fallen in the West and was rapidly coming apart elsewhere. Alexandria had ceased to be a center of high culture in the East. Except for Constantinople there was no true center of culture in what remained of the Graeco-Roman world. The Arabian peninsula was crisscrossed by representatives of two great religions, Judaism and Christianity. Neither religion appealed to the moonworshiping Arabs, but they were to become the bases for a new religion, Islam, which was brought to the Arabs by Mohammed, a child of the Quraysh tribe, who was born in southern Arabia around 571.

When he was a young man, Mohammed married Khadijah, the wealthy widow of a merchant, and soon this young trader had time for contemplation. He turned to a new religion, created a book for it called the Koran, and began to gather followers. In 615 he and his followers fled, for their safety, into Abyssinia. The total following of Islam then consisted of some 94 families. Seven years later Mohammed returned to Medina, and in 628 he led a military raid against Mecca. Before he died five years later this trader had fully established a religion that was to sweep to the shores of the Pacific on the east and to the Atlantic on the west.

On the death of Mohammed the Ummayyad caliphate was established as the political and religious headquarters of Islam, in Damascus. The Arabs moved east against the Persians, and west into Spain, where by the middle of the eighth century they had conquered half the land, taking hundreds of thousands of slaves from Spain and Africa. Slaves, the great wealth of the Mediterranean, and the easy life which now came so suddenly to the warriors of Islam set them fighting among themselves. The Ummayyad caliphate was overthrown by the Abbasid tribe. In 747 the revolt ended and except for one man, the Ummayyads were exterminated. Eighty members of the Ummayyad house were invited to dinner one night by the Abbasids and murdered. The caliphate was then moved to Baghdad.

The same luxury and wealth which led to the constant warring between leaders of the Arab world also brought about the rapid growth of a new culture in the Middle East. Baghdad, one of the great cities of the world, was built by the Arabs. The palace lay in the middle of the city, surrounded by a succession of walls and a deep moat, all circular in design, which caused it to be called the Round City. Four highways fanned out like the spokes of a wheel to the four corners of the Arab empire. The dome of the audience chamber of the great palace rose to a height of 130 feet. At the end of the eighth century, while Europe was disorganized and living in the Dark Ages, Harun al-Rashid maintained the most lavish court in the world. The Arabs had conquered the Persians in 641 and had assimilated much of Persian civilization in the century that followed.

It was through Persia, apparently, as much as through Alexandria, that the Arabs became familiar with the philosophies and science of the ancient Greeks. Two centuries before the Arabs conquered Persia, a sect of Christians had arisen—the Nestorians—who were unwelcome in the Western world because they did not accept Rome's doctrines. The Nestorians moved to Persia where they found sanctuary. They brought with them many Greek books, and the Persian king, Chosroes Nūshīrwan, subsidized translations of both Greek and Sanskrit writings from India into Syriac. By the time the Arabs arrived, Syriac was truly a language of culture.

THE METROPOLITAN MUSEUM OF ART
ROGERS FUND, 1913

Leaf from a manuscript of Dioscorides: a recipe for cough medicine being prepared by a doctor

From 750 to 850 occurred what historian Philip K. Hitti calls "the epoch of translation." During that period wealthy Arab caliphs subsidized the translation of thousands of books. Translators were well paid and protected. One is known to have received payment in gold equal in weight to that of each book he translated, plus the equivalent of a thousand dollars a month in salary. Thus were preserved the works of Aristotle, Galen, Ptolemy, and other scientists of ancient times, when the works of those authors were often lost in the original Greek.

There was a certain amount of direct Hellenic contact with the Arab world, particularly in the beginning when the Ummayyad dynasty was in control, because the Ummayyads had been soldiers of Rome's Byzantine empire in Syria before they took over control of the region. The Ummayyads brought educated men to Damascus and founded an astronomical observatory there in the earliest part of the eighth century. But the major emphasis was to come from the Persian-oriented Arabs of the East.

The first Abbasid caliph was a butcher who invented the practice of spreading a leather carpet at the side of his throne. The carpet was for the royal executioner, who was kept busy in the first days of the Abbasid caliphate. But the second Abbasid caliph, al-Mansur, the founder of Baghdad, was a gentler man. When he arrived in Baghdad, he settled down to build an empire of the conquests that had been made, and to enrich the sciences.

Arabs who came to Baghdad discovered that the people there were familiar with the Siddhantha, the astronomical work of the Hindus of India. There was, even then, a certain cultural contact between the Far Easterners and the people of Baghdad. An Indian astronomer named

Manka was presented to al-Mansur in 773. Al-Mansur's successor, Harun al-Rashid, undertook the collection of original Greek manuscripts for translation. The golden age of Arabic science began in the ninth century, under the caliphate of al-Mamun, who established a "house of wisdom" for the translation of the works of the past from both Occident and Orient. Al-Mamun also built a library and an astronomical observatory, and set his scientists about measuring the obliquity of the ecliptic and preparing star charts.

Al-Farghani was the first of these astronomers. He was followed by al-Battani and Thabit ibn Qurra. These were great names in the world of letters in Islam, and they were to become great names in Europe, as their work eventually trickled into the West. Al-Battani was known particularly for his accurate observations of the heavenly bodies and for his catalogue of fixed stars. Thabit ibn Qurra was a great translator, as well as an astronomer.

About this time in Baghdad a mathematician named al-Khwarizmi undertook the study of arithmetic and mathematics brought from the Indian civilization to the east of Islam. At the same time he studied the geometry and higher mathematics brought to Islam from the Greeks of the West. His great contribution to the future was in putting together parts of both of these studies, along with his own contributions. His arithmetic used the Hindu numeral system, which has come down through the ages, known as the Arabic system because al-Khwarizmi gave it to the Western world. He also is responsible for the term algebra for description of a kind of mathematics, and his system of algebra gave solutions to many problems. Al-Khwarizmi was also a geographer, and he improved on the geography of Ptolemy before passing it on. He may have been involved in the effort to measure the circumference of the earth which was undertaken on the great plain north of the Euphrates River in the time of al-Mamun's caliphate.

In mathematics, the contribution of these Arabs of the East is apparent. In astronomy, one of their greatest achievements was preserving the works of Ptolemy and passing them on with the additional observations and star charts they had amassed, and in bringing some of the work of the Indians to the West. The book of al-Battani, called in Latin *De scientia stellarum,* was used as a text-book in Europe until the middle of the Renaissance.

The Arabs contributed heavily to many scientific fields in this period, serving as synthesists between East and West. Paper, for example, was brought to the Moslem world in the eighth century. In the battle of Samarkand in 704 several Chinese papermakers were captured. In 751 a paper mill was established at Samarkand, and forty years afterward, another was built at Baghdad. It took a hundred years before another mill was built in Egypt, and two hundred years more for one to be built in Spain. Then, in 1189, a mill was built north of the Pyrenees mountains, and paper truly had made its way to Europe.

The use of paper progressed slowly, but so did scientific knowledge in this period. The Arabs saved it and incubated it, and helped it grow while science in the West barely held on in the Dark Ages. But superstition and nonsense existed in the Arab world as well as in the West, as can be seen by a glimpse of the rise of alchemy under the Arabs. In the ninth century there lived a person named Jabir ibn Hayyan, who was later to be known to Europeans as a mystical genius in the field of alchemy. Actually, most of the papers attributed to him turn out to be not the writings of one man at all, but of a number of members of a mystic sect called the Brethren of Purity. These brethren held that all the world was a mystery, and that mankind represented a tiny replica of the whole universe. They said that all metals and all else were formed by the interaction of the principles of mercury and sulphur, and they set out, using an old Greek princi- ple involving four elements, to change the nature of metals. This was much the same as the gold-making of the Alexandrians, and it was also quite similar to a Chinese practice of about this period. But these early alchemists, in simply working with chemicals, handed down a tradition that was to be valuable in the true science of chemistry.

There was no shortage of students of many scientific subjects. Abul Wafa studied practical problems of geom- etry and trigonometry. Later Omar Khayyam improved on the mathematics of al-Khwarizmi, although Khayyam has come to be known to us as a poet rather than as a mathe- matician. Al-Biruni determined the relative densities of a number of metals and precious stones; he studied hydro- statics and mathematics. Many of these men were to pro- duce great works in more fields than one. Such a man was Ibn Sina, a Moslem scientist who was born in central Asia in 980, and who, like Aristotle, was so learned that his life and works were surrounded by an aura of mystery. This man was to be known to western Europe later as Avicenna, and it is believed by certain historians that his thought represented the climax of medieval philosophy. He was a doctor and a philosopher, noted for his encyclopedia which was preserved and translated for European use in later centuries, just as the encyclopedia of astronomy by al-Biruni was saved.

The period of Arab political ascendancy in Baghdad was brief. By 820 A.D. the Caliph of Baghdad had more power in his hands than any other man in the world. A hundred years later a successor had so little power that he could scarcely control the quarreling of tribesmen just outside the city. The administration of the caliphate had failed in every way. The Arabs had not truly created inter-

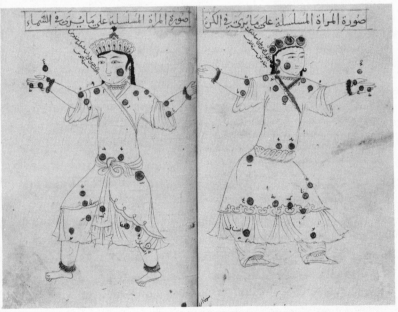

THE METROPOLITAN MUSEUM OF ART
ROGERS FUND, 1913

Illustrations of the constellation Andromeda from a manuscript on astronomy, tenth century A.D.

nationalism. They still fought among themselves. Their harem and slave systems had weakened their society. The strong rule of the old emperors was replaced by that of the luxury-loving Saljuq Turks in 1037 when Tughril became caliph, but the cultural level of Eastern Islam was dropping. At this time knowledgeable men of scientific bent began to move westward within the Arab lands.

In 1216 a new era began. Jenghiz Khan, with 60,000 Mongolian troops, stormed through Eastern Islam, killing and burning. Bukhara, Samarkand, and finally Baghdad were invaded and their people butchered, the latter city by Hulagu Khan in 1258. The caliph was put to death, along with his entire court, but Baghdad was not destroyed as had been the other cities of Islam, because Hulagu established his own capital there. True, the mosques were at first used to stable Mongol horses, but less than half a century after Hulagu's death Mongols were worshiping in these same mosques. The conquered had won a victory, and Islam became the state religion of the Mongol hordes.

Hulagu and his children interested themselves in scientific affairs once again. Hulagu founded an observatory in Azerbaidjan, south of Tabriz, under Nasir al-Din al-Tusi, the court's grand vizier who was also an astronomer. A library of some four hundred thousand volumes was gathered in this place, and astronomers from China and from Spain mingled there. At this observatory a new set of astronomical tables was compiled, including materials derived from Greek, Chinese, Persian, and Arabic sources. Many improved instruments were used, and the workshop of the observatory was known throughout the Moslem world for its accuracy. Nasir al-Din al-Tusi wrote widely on geography, philosophy, medicine, and theology as well as on astronomy and mathematics. This was not Arabic science any more, of course, but Tartar. It still had much of the tradition of Arabic science, and it was built on the same roots. It continued in the East for several hundred years more. Ulugh Begh, grandson of Tamerlane, also took an interest in scientific affairs in the beginning of his reign in 1394 and established a fine observatory at Samarkand. Here were brought many astronomers. The stars were again studied and their positions fixed on maps. The observations of the astronomers of Ulugh Begh at the observatory were the most accurate yet made by mankind.

The story of the contribution of the Arabs to science is illustrated very well in the field of medical science. The medicine of Rome was never Roman, but Greek, and when Rome's power failed, the center of Roman medicine moved first to Constantinople, and there it decayed. Still, it did not die. The Romans of Byzantium continued to learn and to practice medicine, but they did not make any great leaps forward. Alexander of Tralles, one of the great Byzantine doctors, and Paul of Aegina were among the last ancients to be known to history for major medical accomplishments, and they lived in the sixth century, long after the decline of Western Rome. Alexander was an experienced physician, but he knew little of anatomy or physiology. His major work was in internal diseases, and he wrote twelve books on that subject which were translated into Arabic. Also translated were the books by Paul of Aegina, who had studied at Alexandria and then at Rome. His work consisted largely of an encyclopedic treatment of Roman medical knowledge. If one doubts that the Romans had much medical knowledge, Arturo Castiglioni notes that they could operate successfully on such difficult diseases as cancer.

The Nestorians were as important in the perpetuation of medical knowledge as they had been in keeping alive knowledge of astronomy and mathematics. When they left Constantinople for the East, they established medical schools at several points along their path to Persia. When the Arabs began their conquest, they took an immediate interest in these schools.

One important Arabic contribution to medical science was the return to the Hippocratic idea that experience, logic, and nature could do much to heal the sick. Some historians have felt that the Arabs contributed nothing to medicine except to keep it alive, and that while they were doing so the Christian church was also keeping it alive in the Greek tradition. But medical historians of another school believe that the Arabs contributed greatly to medicine by saving the works of the ancients (as they did in all science) and by their strong interest in the chemical processes. One of the foremost physicians of the Arab world was al-Rhazi (known to the West as Rhazes) who has been called the greatest doctor of Islam and of all the Middle Ages. Rhazes was a Persian who moved to Baghdad in the time of the Arab dominance there. He was supposedly mistreated by one ruler when some chemical experiments failed, and the order was given that Rhazes be beaten on the head with a book until either the book or the physician's head was broken. He was blinded as a result, so the story goes.

Although Rhazes wrote more than two hundred books on medicine, philosophy, religion, mathematics, and astronomy, he is famous chiefly as a medical man. His most important book was an encyclopedia of medical practice called *al-Hawi,* which set forth all the medical knowledge of the world of Islam in the tenth century. He also wrote a book on smallpox, which he had observed at close hand. Rhazes was followed by Avicenna, who was to be the most honored Arab doctor in Europe, and by Isaac Judaeus of Tunisia, an eminent oculist, doctor, and teacher who paved the way for a rebirth of Arabic scientific study in Egypt (which represents an aspect of Arab science different from that known in Baghdad).

In 909 a group of Moslems broke away from the Abbasid caliphate in Baghdad and established the Fatimid caliphate in Tunis. Soon they controlled all of North Africa, including Egypt, and Egypt entered her fourth period of scientific progress. It was to last only two hundred years, but in that period, as the strength of Baghdad declined, many scientists from the Moslem world sought refuge in the greater freedom of this bridge between Eastern and Western Islam. In Tunis the Fatimid caliph, al-Hakim, established a "house of science" in 995. To this city came the great al-Haitham, or Alhazen as he was to be known in the West. He had been born at Basra, but with the decline of the Abbasids he moved to North Africa. Alhazen has been called the "true physicist" of medieval Islam, as Archimedes had been in Greek times. Alhazen combined experiment with mathematical analysis, particularly in the study of optics. He made his own mirrors of steel, and he conducted studies of refraction of light, by both physical investigation and the use of mathematics.

Alhazen held views about the science of optics quite different from those of his Greek predecessors. Euclid and Ptolemy had both studied optics extensively. Also, both had come to the conclusion that the eye sends forth rays of light in order to see—something like the beams of an automobile's headlights. Alhazen held, however, that the source of the light was not the eye but the object seen. He studied the characteristics of magnifying glasses and corrected the theory of Ptolemy about refraction of light. Another Arab, al-Masudi of Cairo, wrote an encyclopedia of natural history, and the astronomer Ibn Yunis gathered records of observations made during the previous two hundred years, and before he died in 1009 he named his new set of tables for the Caliph al-Hakim.

Although their civilization was already declining, the Arabs seemed to be at the height of their scientific effort around the year 1000. Contrasts between the East and the West were very great. For a thousand years, from 500 A.D. to 1500 A.D., the technology and civilization of the East was superior to that of the West. During nearly all this period, the best products available came from the Near East. Silks, mosaics, ivory, Persian ceramics, Egyptian glass, Syrian metalwork—all these were highly regarded in the Western world, which acknowledged that it could produce nothing nearly so fine.

Where did Islam's culture come from? It came from the Far East and from the Byzantine Empire, which was Roman and Greek, and from the Nestorians, Syrians, and Jews. But again, this was essentially a Greek culture. In many ways the roots were the same for East and West. Aristotle was translated into Syriac, Arabic, and Latin— nevertheless he was still to be the common scientific and cultural father of Islam and later Christendom.

Technically, the East had a great deal to offer the

West. After paper, other materials were brought to the West, some from as far away as China. The Great Khans had discovered gunpowder in use in China, and had spared the lives of the Chinese technicians of a gunpowder factory in order that they might learn the technique of making this implement of war. It is possible that printing also came from the East. In any case, playing cards that had been printed in the Orient were known in the West long before printing was adopted in Europe. The stern-post rudder and the compass apparently also came from the East, as did the fore-and-aft rig for boats and ships.

The Arabic system of numerals, which originated in India, was brought to Europe, finally, in the end of the twelfth century by a merchant of Pisa named Leonardo Fibonacci, who had learned the system from traders in North Africa. This actually represents a degree of technology, but it was vital to the development of science in the West. Besides those numerals, which spread relatively quickly across Europe, the Arabs offered major contributions to the West in astrology, astronomy, mathematics, and alchemy.

The Moslems adopted alchemy with great enthusiasm once they had learned its principles from the writings of the Lesser Democritus and others. Following Geber and Rhazes, they made strides in what might be termed the scientific aspect of alchemy. Rhazes, for example, classified materials into animal, vegetable, and mineral substances. In addition, he made subclassifications of minerals, differentiating between spirits, salts, and others. It was perhaps not a long step scientifically, but it was a step forward to classify substances, even wrongly, because the classification was based on the plan of grouping substances according to their properties. The system remained in use until the eighteenth century in Europe.

Moslem alchemists were also familiar with a number of compounds, such as cinnabar, white and red lead, ferric oxide, and wine vinegar. It is believed that they had determined a manner of making acetic acid from vinegar.

It is apparent, then, that the debt of the West to the East was large where it concerned science and scientific thought. The methods of transmission of this information were varied, ranging from the return of crusaders with captives, slaves, and booty to the quiet travels of peaceful traders. It is true that early in the period of Islam, the Caliphate at Baghdad had certain contacts with Charlemagne, the first of the Holy Roman Emperors, but the main sources of information about Moslem culture and the ancient culture of the West were to be found in Spain. There East and West met in the Iberian peninsula, in North Africa, where the West came to trade, and in Italy and Sicily, which maintained a strong Moslem influence for a long period.

CHAPTER **11**

The Arabs of the West

ONE day in the year 750 two young survivors of the Abbasid massacres of the Ummayyad dynasty of the Arab world were hiding from their enemies in a Bedouin camp on the banks of the Euphrates River, when suddenly into the camp rode a group of horsemen carrying the black standards of the Abbasids. The two boys leapt into the river and began to swim away. The younger boy, who was thirteen years old, heeding promises from those on the bank that he would be safe if he returned, swam back to shore and immediate assassination. The older boy, whose name was Abd-al-Rahman, knew the fate that faced him, and he kept on swimming against the strong current until he reached the other side of the river and safety.

Abd-al-Rahman then set his feet on a path to the southwest, headed for North Africa, where he had relatives who would help him, and where he would be as far away from the long arm of the Abbasid caliph as he could flee and still remain in the Arab world. He went to Palestine and there, helped by a solitary friend, he set off for North Africa, where he was nearly assassinated by the governor of the province after he was recognized as an Ummayyad from his aquiline features and his bright red hair. Finally, after hiding for five years in North Africa, he reached Ceuta, across the Strait of Gibraltar from Spain, where his family had originated. His uncles still lived in this stronghold of the Berbers, and they gave him sanctuary.

But this fierce survivor of the Ummayyads did not want only sanctuary. As soon as he could, he made his way across the Strait and called on the loyalty of the Syrian troops from Damascus who were stationed there. Those Damascenes had always been loyal followers of the Ummayyads, since the first caliphate, and they flocked to this symbol of the old ruling house. One enemy stronghold after another fell to the Ummayyad leader and his followers. In 755 Abd-al-Rahman established the independent kingdom of Andalusia, and he continued to lay waste to the lands and treasures of the Abbasids. When the Abbasid Caliph of Baghdad appointed a governor and dispatched him to Spain to conquer the Ummayyad upstart, Abd-al-Rahman sent the governor's head back to his master, preserved in salt and camphor and wrapped in the governor's papers of appointment.

Abd-al-Rahman carried the Arab tide as far as it would go in Europe, to the slopes of the Pyrenees. Worried about the chance of an Arab breakthrough into France, Charlemagne sent a force under Roland to drive the Arabs back. The Arabs were defeated in one great battle, and apparently Abd-al-Rahman realized that to cross the Pyrenees he would have to maintain impossible lines of communication, as well as face strong enemies. The Arab push into Europe ended in Spain.

Seven years after his escape on the banks of the Euphrates, Abd-al-Rahman had consolidated his holdings in Spain to the point where he could settle down in luxury and pursue the arts. He built his palace at Cordova and set out, as had Alexander the Great, to weld his mixture of races into a nation. He also undertook a program of public works which was to make Cordova into a splendid city, and he began to attract scholars to this outpost. A third of his royal revenue was devoted to public works, which included lighting of the streets so that one could walk for miles at night beneath the lights, and to the establishment of universities. It was the boast of the caliphs of Cordova that while European kings could scarcely write their names, the slaves of Western Islam were literate. Abd-al-Rahman III, who ruled from 912 to 961, was an enlightened king who made Cordova the most cultured city in Europe. In his day Cordova boasted 70 libraries, more than a hundred thousand homes, and twenty-one suburbs in which the people lived under conditions regarded as luxurious in the Christian capitals of Europe.

Under Abd-al-Rahman's caliphate Spain was one of the most populous countries of Europe. Besides the material goods of wealth, the Arabs brought new technologies and science to the country. They introduced fine leatherwork, silk and silkworms, glassware, ceramics industries, and the art of inlaying steel and other metals. They also brought advanced agricultural methods, and new farming equipment.

The University of Cordova was founded in the great

mosque built by the first Abd-al-Rahman, and it welcomed students from all the Arab world—even Christians were noted among the scholars there. The next caliph, al-Hakim, so increased the glory of Moslem Spain that it was compared with the splendor and high cultural level achieved by the Abbasids under al-Mamun in Baghdad a hundred and fifty years earlier. Cordova was called the "jewel of the world," and there the caliphs amassed a library of some four hundred thousand volumes.

Medicine began to flourish early in the golden period of Moslem Spain. Hasdai ibn Shaprut was one famous physician. Another, known to Westerners as Abul Kasim, wrote a medical encyclopedia. It was prepared in thirty sections, dealing with the medical arts, surgery, and medicines. Abul Kasim was regarded as the most important Arab writer on surgery.

In 948 Abd-al-Rahman III received a precious medical book, written in Greek, from the Emperor of Byzantium. As Greek was then practically unknown in Cordova the emperor sent along the monk Nicholas of Cordova to translate the work. With the Jewish physician Hasdai ibn Shaprut, who was minister to Abd al-Rahman, the monk translated into Arabic all the names of the plants in this book written by the ancient Greek, Dioscorides. Thus began a great tradition which was to help bring knowledge that seemed half lost into the hands of the Christian world of Europe. Later, many translations were to be made by groups of three men—a Christian, a Moslem, and a Jew. The Jew was important because he knew both Latin and Arabic, and probably a handful of other languages as well.

The translation, made in 948 by the Byzantine monk

Nicholas and the Spanish Jew, Hasdai ibn Shaprut, was amended a few years later by ibn Golgol, who also wrote widely in the medical field. A number of the physicians of this time were also philosophers and students of other sciences. Ibn al-Wafid was the caliph's minister of state in the eleventh century, and a physician at the same time. Al-Bakri of Cordova was a doctor and a geographer. Ali ibn Isa, another physician, specialized in diseases of the eye (which were very common in the Moslem world). He wrote a book on the subject which became the standard text in Islam and the West and was used for many centuries afterward by Moslems throughout the world.

In the West, a prominent astronomer was al-Zarkali of Cordova, who prepared the Toletan astronomical tables of 1080. Generally speaking, the astronomers of Islam added to the technology of astronomy by improving the instruments used, and to the body of astronomical knowledge by very accurate measurements. They were better known in this regard than for theory of astronomical movement in the heavens, but al-Zarkali was something of an exception. He suggested that Mercury might have an elliptical movement rather than a totally circular one.

Ptolemy's system disturbed the Moslem scientists because they wanted to find an explanation of the movements of the heavenly bodies which they could accept as real and accurate—not a mathematical explanation that did not explain everything. They wanted perfect unity. So, the Arabs of the West again turned to philosophy to begin their studies. They first studied the works of Aristotle, and then they began to seek an acceptable system for the universe.

The movement began early in the twelfth century.

It was brought into focus by Abul Walid Muhammed ibn Rushd, better known to the Western world as Averroës. He was born in Andalusia and later became governor of that area of the caliphate. He was the author of a work on Aristotle which affected Western European thinking deeply during the Middle Ages. He and other philosophers of a similar turn of mind rejected the idea of epicycles because they turned about a geometrical point. Instead, they tried to work out a system based on the Eudoxian principle of homocentric spheres, which Aristotle explained in his works.

The tide of Islam was receding by this time. Toledo fell to the Christians in 1085 and the Moslems began a slow, inching retreat, there and elsewhere in the Mediterranean. A few years before, Norman invaders had captured the island of Sicily from the Moslems, and Roger I, son of Tancred de Hauteville, became king of the land, with his court established at Palermo. Here was a strange kingdom in which a Christian king ruled, many Moslems held positions of power, and the king's wife issued orders in Greek and Arabic. Roger patronized Arab learning and surrounded himself with Arab scientists and philosophers. The Christian courtiers wore Moslem clothing and adopted many Moslem practices.

Roger II's court was the home of al-Drisi, the most important Arab geographer of the Middle Ages who also gained fame by constructing a silver celestial sphere for the king. The important matter, in the twelfth and thirteenth centuries, was that Sicily provided a friendly meeting place where Moslems and Western Christians could gather. The population of Sicily was a great mixture of Greeks, Moslems, and Europeans, all using Latin as the language of learning. Here and in southern Italy, which was also held by these Norman rulers, the work of ancients and of Arabs was translated. As early as the eleventh century traces of Arab learning had moved as far north as the Alps.

The gradual decline of the Arab civilization of the West caused some scholars to move nervously back to points closer to the heart of Islam. (There was little movement back to Baghdad, for the Abbasid caliphate was suffering more serious upheaval than was the West.) Still, not all the important men of science chose to flee Spain. Ibn-Zuhr, later known as Avenzoar, lived in Seville until well past the middle of the twelfth century. At the request of Averroës this physician wrote a number of treatises on medical matters. He even went so far as to question some of the conclusions of Galen, which was almost unheard of in that day. His writings were to influence the West for five hundred years.

The greatest of Arab botanists was a pharmacist named al-Baitar. He traveled extensively throughout the Moslem world, searching out plants, medicines, and compounds. Al-Baitar wrote two books, one about plants from the point of view of natural history, the other about plants from the point of view of pharmaceuticals or drugs. He combined the earlier work of Dioscorides and of Galen, and he made many personal observations and descriptions of more than 1,400 drugs—three hundred of them for the first time in history.

One of the physicians and students who chose to leave Moslem Spain was Abu Imram Musa ibn Maimun, known as Maimonides. He apparently was a victim of persecution in Spain and came to Cairo where there was less irritation and greater freedom during the troublesome period of the twelfth century. Maimonides was a Jewish theologian. He was also a philosopher and a physician who wrote widely on the subject of hygiene. When he came to Cairo, the Fatimid dynasty had been overthrown by Salah al-Din, known to Westerners as Saladin. Maimonides was appointed his court physician. He provided written descriptions of several medical problems which had not been treated on before, including certain poisons and their antidotes and the testing of the pulse. Maimonides became a celebrated hero, for his religious works and for his near martyrdom. His tomb is located at Tiberias, in the Holy Land, and is still regarded as a sanctuary by the Jews. In Cairo for centuries sick Jews often spent a night in the crypt in the synagogue named for him. They were practicing the ancient *incubation,* which began even before the Asclepieia, in which the ill sought places of holiness or worship in order to rid themselves of their sickness.

The collapse of the Arab world was gradual in the West, and this permitted the transmission of knowledge to the Christian world in several ways and through several routes. By the middle of the thirteenth century much of Spain was restored to the hands of Westerners. Alfonso of Castile encouraged the spread of Moslem knowledge in the territory he captured from the Moslems. After the tenth century the studies of astronomy and astrology were cultivated in Spain, and the astronomical tables prepared by the Arabs were only slightly modified later, when in the thirteenth century they became known as the Alfonsine tables of Alfonso X.

The debt of the West to the Arabs is great in the field

of astronomy, even in the origin of some words. The word azimuth is taken from the Arabic *al-sumut;* nadir comes from *nazir;* zenith comes from *al-samt,* and many of the stars' names are of Arabic origin.

Even as the Arab culture declined it continued to produce positive results in science until the fifteenth century. Al-Hasan al Marrakushi wrote on the use of trigonometry to solve astronomical problems, using such refined instruments as the quadrant, astrolabe, and planisphere. Abu'l Faraj summarized Ptolemy's *Almagest,* which helped that great astronomical study of antiquity become popular in a slowly awakening European culture. Ibn al Banna, another Arab mathematician, wrote a study of the use of Hindu numerals, which helped make them popular in the West.

Most of this material, and hundreds of other books, began to trickle into western Europe through Sicily and Spain, after the tenth century, some coming direct from North Africa, and other material following the even more difficult route from the Abbasid region and through eastern Europe. But many such manuscripts did not come west, particularly those which originated in and around Baghdad, and some were not to be discovered until the Western penetration of India in the seventeenth century, by which time the West had made many of the same discoveries.

Much scientific writing was lost, as always when warring cultures meet. Philip Hitti, historian of the Arabs, notes that after the destruction of Arab power in Spain less than two thousand of the hundreds of thousands of volumes survived to be collected by Philip II and used to form the nucleus of the Escorial library near Madrid.

What had happened to the rest of these volumes? Some had been taken back to the heart of Islam by retreating scholars of the Arab world. Some had been destroyed in fighting, or lost during the capture and looting of cities. Others had already made their way to the West. By the end of the thirteenth century, Arab science and philosophy —and that of the ancient world—had been transmitted into Europe. The route led from Toledo through the Pyrenees, the Provençal countryside of France, and into Lorraine, Germany, and Central Europe and across the English Channel. In eastern France, the Abbey at Cluny housed many fleeing Spanish monks, and during the twelfth century Cluny became a focal point for the spread of Arab sciences. In 1141 the first translation of the Koran was made there, apparently on the principle that it was wise to know something of the enemy and his beliefs.

As the Christians advanced into Spain, the Arabs moved south, until finally they were ringed around the Alhambra of Granada for a last stand in Europe. They left Spain as Columbus was sailing for the Indies, using maps that followed the projection of Ptolemy, which the West had reacquired from the Arabs.

In the twelfth century the Christian church rallied the strength of Europe in an attempt to seize control of the Holy Land. The First Crusade reached Jerusalem, and Western European colonies were established in the heart of the Moslem world. Where there was any sort of peace, the Westerners learned the sciences of the Arabs, and that process continued until the Westerners were driven out by Saladin.

But scientific knowledge also came via more peaceful means. Alfonso of Spain, known as El Sabio (the Learned),

Emperor Frederick II of Sicily, and Archbishop Raymond I of Toledo were all instrumental, from the European point of view, in bringing about an interchange of culture. Frederick secured translations of certain works of Aristotle and Averroës and sent them to Bologna and to Paris. He also asked the Moslem scholars technical questions, such as why oar blades, under water, appear to be bent. Frederick undertook a study of zoology on his own, thereby displaying the renewed interest with which many men of public affairs had begun to regard the world around them.

Alfonso subsidized many translations of scientific works, in addition to the Alfonsine tables of astronomy. In 1276 he ordered an encyclopedia to be made on the subject of astronomical instruments. All the knowledge then available on that subject was brought together in one set of books.

Translations in Spain were often made from Arabic to Castilian to Latin. Some were made into Hebrew and Portuguese. In Sicily, a number of translations were made directly into Latin, which was a handier process.

Some of the famous translators of the twelfth century were John of Seville, Robert of Chester, and Adelard of Bath, who translated Euclid's geometrical work into Latin from Arabic, as well as the revised work of al-Khwarizmi which brought trigonometry to Europe; Robert of Chester translated al-Khwarizmi's algebra into Latin.

Gerard of Cremona is one of the most famous translators of all time, and perhaps he was not so much a translator himself as an executive. Historians of science, noting the works for which he is given credit, say he could not possibly have done so much by himself. He, too, translated Euclid, and in 1175 translated the *Almagest* of Ptolemy, and Ibn Sina's medical works, which were to become texts in the famous Italian medical schools at Milan and Padua. Gerard also translated much of Aristotle's work.

Translation was slow work, but it proceeded year after year, and the unfolding of new knowledge seemed to stimulate the half-educated to greater efforts. Not all this was accomplished without pain, however, for in the Christian world of the West there was much animosity against the Moslems. In the ninth century, certain Christian leaders complained bitterly that Spanish Christians were studying works in Arabic. It has been suggested that because of this attitude Westerners lost many opportunities to learn of the ways of the East. Toledo, for example, remained a stronghold of Christianity throughout the Moslem period, but there only a few advanced students made any attempt to learn and transmit their learning to the other lands of Europe. Men of the West, although engaged in a religious struggle with Islam, stopped at Constantinople early in the thirteenth century to sack the once great capital of Byzantium. They even occupied Constantinople from 1204 to 1261, but they made little or no attempt to translate the priceless Greek volumes in the libraries there.

Thus, not all of the works of the Arab scholars were translated early. Indeed, some still remained untranslated in the middle of the twentieth century, and discoveries that dealt with the circulation of the blood, made by Arabs hundreds of years ago, were not transmitted to the Western world, which had to find its own way, slowly and arduously.

What had been transmitted, then? Largely, through the process of selection by the translators, the works of the old Greek and Roman scholars were preferred to those of unknown ancestry, or to those originally written by an Arab or a student from farther east. The Europeans were eager to go back to their own beginnings, and that is the course they followed.

Still, in the process many new ideas entered Europe from afar. The magnetic compass, having made its way from China to the Middle East, was adopted by the West. Gunpowder also found its way to Europe, while on the other hand the medical theories of Ibn al-Nafis were forgotten in the revival of Galen. About this same time the wheelbarrow and cast iron appeared suddenly in Europe. The stage was being readied for a full-scale revival of interest in learning by the eleventh century, and although many of the old ways of doing things were to persist for centuries longer, gradually they began to break down. Islam, which had reached its crest before the end of the tenth century, was to give ground before a number of conquerors, including Tamerlane who sacked Damascus and captured Ankara. The superior civilization of the Arabs was submerged beneath the harsh rule of the Ottoman Turks in the sixteenth century. These Ottomans had come from Mongolia, had mixed with the tribes of central Asia, and had grown wise in the ways of war, even if inclined to luxury and not to the pursuit of knowledge.

In 1516 the Arab armies of the Mamelukes and the Turks met near Aleppo and the Ottomans defeated the

Arabs overwhelmingly. Shortly thereafter Syria fell into Turkish hands. A year later Egypt's power was crushed and Cairo, once a center of knowledge, became a provincial trading center. Mecca and Medina were swallowed up. Damascus wilted, as did all Arabia, when the focus of Moslem power moved to Constantinople. The cruelties, heavy taxes, and excesses of the Turkish rulers wiped out the fruits of a thousand years of Arab knowledge and superior culture, with the same apparent ease that had been shown in the destruction of Greek civilization, and in a far shorter period of time.

CHAPTER 12

Europe in the Dark Ages

THE Arab contribution to science up to the sixteenth century was enormous, but the Arab story does not tell what happened in Europe from the time of Ptolemy and Galen, in the second century. What did happen during those centuries? Very little, and that is a story in itself, because there were definite reasons for the decline of the effort of Europeans to understand the world around them.

Something took the place of human curiosity during this period in Europe. That something was religion, which replaced questioning. The Christian religion was the major faith. But there were others—sun worship, and a continued belief in a pantheon of gods who became ever more mysterious and needed ever more blind faith and attention. It was an attitude that had been developing from the mixing of Greek, Babylonian, Egyptian, and native Roman cultures. It would not be proper to say that religion could not flourish in an atmosphere of curiosity, but it is proper to say that the zealots who led the religious movements did not believe religion could survive questioning. The evangelical nature of Christianity in this time of the great spread of the religion led its followers to devote their full attention to the religious work at hand. A few centuries after the rise of Christianity the almost simultaneous rise of the Moslem religion and Arabic science proved that religion alone could not be blamed for the decline of the spirit of science and all other knowledge in the West. It was a general decline, which can be traced to a period two hundred years before the fall of the great capital of Rome to the barbarians.

In medicine, Rome produced no one of importance to history after Galen, who died in the year 200. In astronomy, Ptolemy's work in the second century brought Western knowledge to a temporary climax. In mathematics, Theon of Alexandria persisted in development of thought until about the year 400, but he was a rarity. In physics, alchemy, botany, and all the other scientific specialties known in the periods of Greece and Rome, there was no figure to match those of the older periods. One might put the end of ancient science and the beginning of the Middle Ages at the end of the fourth century or beginning of the fifth century.

The *kind* of writings that were saved from the past make it apparent that the point of view of the men who preserved them was not one that would lead to further independent discoveries. The works of Plato, the philosopher, were largely lost to Europe, but saved was a commentary on his *Timaeus*, which held a thoroughly dogmatic view of the universe. Man—the microcosm—was a tiny being that was almost exactly the same as the universe in its whole—the macrocosm. Obviously, such a view lent itself to every variety of magic, mystic, and superstitious belief. This was the basis of the view of the universe held by Europeans throughout the Dark Ages. Very little remained of Aristotle—again, this was the effect of the decision of the translators from the Greek. What did remain was Aristotle's logical work, not his great studies of natural history, which might have kindled the interest of some in the animal life around them. The ancient works on botany were lost, because no one translated them into the languages the people could understand. Some mathematical works were retained—consequently mathematics in Europe did not slip as far back as did the other scientific studies.

But in scientific thought there was virtually no advance in Europe until the middle of the sixteenth century. Among general historians of the nineteenth century it was popular to indicate that a sudden, sharp break had occurred with the fall of Rome, and that scientific knowledge in western Europe then shattered and was almost totally lost until the Renaissance, when knowledge was "reborn" in all its forms. Later historians note that this new growth of science was much more gradual and much less obvious than envisaged by earlier historians. Perhaps the process was begun by a state of mind. Besides matters of religious zest, and the arbitrary stands that it produces, there was the question of the approach of educated men in the late days of Rome. Those whose writings came down through the ages set a pattern, and that pattern was generalism. This continued throughout the Middle Ages.

One of the most famous of these generalists was Boeth-

ius, who lived in Rome between 480 and 524, when he
was put to death for intrigue against the emperor, Theodoric the Ostrogoth. Boethius was a vital figure in the history of science and knowledge, not so much for what he
did, but for what he might have done. Had he chosen to
translate different works, such as those of Ptolemy, Hipparchus, Theophrastus, or the natural science of Aristotle,
the Western world might have been a different place during the next thousand years. But Boethius contented himself with describing, not probing. He was a man of his time
and he shared the interests and views of his time. He was
an encyclopedist. He tried to cover as large an area of
knowledge as possible, and ended with very little substance. So did many others.

Around 500 Martianus Capella translated a number of
works and compiled from them an encyclopedia, whose
contributions to knowledge were contained in seven books
(two others were devoted to an allegory). Here was established the classification of studies that was to remain with
Europe throughout the Middle Ages. The studies included
grammar, dialectic, rhetoric, geometry, arithmetic, astronomy, and music.

Pliny's *Natural History* was retained, but this, an encyclopedia, was not an original work. And so the encyclopedists translated other abbreviated works. With each
abbreviation a certain amount of the knowledge was submerged. This practice continued throughout the age.

The fact that the earth was round, however, was never
lost to students in the depths of the Dark Ages, as has
sometimes been stated. In Capella's encyclopedia, the
section on astronomy contains an indication that the sun
was the center of the universe as the ancient Greeks be-

lieved, and that view continued for some time in the Middle Ages, although it was not widely held at the end of the period. Still, a certain, definite knowledge could be gleaned from the encyclopedic writings of the students of an age of decay, and it was. Late in the sixth century, Isidore of Seville wrote an encyclopedia of the sciences. A century later in Britain the Venerable Bede wrote another treatment. In Germany Alcuin passed along the accumulated knowledge of the age. Thus knowledge was not dead in Europe.

Medical science is an area in which the most definite workings of the scientific process can be seen. The progress of medicine gives an indication of the direction of science as a whole. Medicine did not die when Rome was reduced to the status of an ordinary town. The Germanic barbarians had a tradition of magic and demonism in medicine. The physician was a sorcerer who conducted sacrifices and urged demons out of the human body. Herbs were known and were passed down to later generations with song and story. Yet to be effective, these herbs were supposed to be collected only on special days and in special ways.

The first contact of the barbarians with Roman medicine came during the wars, when barbarians saw the Roman legionary medical system in action. They saw Roman hospitals, some were treated in them. The Emperor Theodoric, a barbarian, was not an uncultured man. Before he captured the Western Roman Empire he had lived for a time in Constantinople, a hostage there to guarantee the good behavior of his family and the Ostrogoths. Theodoric fully accepted the Roman medical system, and through him the Roman methods of maintaining public health were retained. As an example, he drained the marshes and began a system under which examinations were held for those who desired to practice lay medicine.

In the sixth century, when the Roman Empire dissolved in a succession of wars and minor campaigns, students of medicine fled to the monasteries and the churches. One of the great monasteries was that of Montecassino, where St. Benedict founded his order of monks, and where a number of educated men came, bringing with them manuscripts which contained a certain amount of the medical knowledge of the past. One of these men, Cassiodorus, recommended studies of the work on herbs by Dioscorides, and of the books of Hippocrates and Galen on the philosophy of medicine and medical treatment. The monastery at Montecassino became noted as a place where medical knowledge was preserved and copies of old manuscripts were made. Later, other Benedictine monks took that knowledge to Oxford, Cambridge, and Winchester in England, to Tours in France, and to Fulda and St. Gall in Germany, where hospitals were soon to be built as parts of the monasteries.

Charlemagne established the cathedral schools in his empire. In 805 he ordered that medicine be taught in these schools, although the program was called physics. The Benedictines, fanning out from Montecassino, carried their knowledge of the ancients with them. Medical instruction was started in the monasteries; at St. Gall, for example, herbs were planted, and a pharmacy was established. The monks also provided a special room for the physician, and arrangements for six ill persons in the monastery.

In the beginning of the Dark Ages there seems to have

been little important medical writing. In the middle of the fifth century a few descriptions of herbs began to appear. By the sixth century medical knowledge in Europe was concentrated in the hands of the clergy, and at this time the use, or even understanding, of Greek disappeared among Western scholars. A few clerics could read the ancients, but only a few, such as the Venerable Bede who wrote on medicine from his monastery at Wearmouth in England.

Another kind of medicine existed in the Dark Ages. The medicine of the monasteries was theoretical as well as practical, while that practiced in the towns and villages by laymen was only practical. It followed the old Roman ideas of health, and while lay medical men were not the scholars of medicine in that period, they diagnosed ills and dosed patients with herbs and other medicines. The medicine of the clergy began to decline toward the tenth century, and afterward the popes and church councils began to restrict the medical activity of the monks and finally forbade it altogether. The practice of medicine took too much of the time of the clergy away from their religious duties.

The first great medical school in Europe was founded at Salerno, south of Naples, just above the top of the instep of the Italian boot. This school was first heard of in the ninth century, and its beginnings were undoubtedly influenced by the establishment of a Benedictine hospital in the area during the seventh century. A legend concerning the school tells that it was begun by four physicians whose native tongues were Greek, Latin, Hebrew, and Arabic. No matter whether or not the legend is true, the influence of the various cultures was there, for Salerno was in the zone of southern Italy which was strongly influenced by Arabic culture from the beginning, and southern Italy and Sicily carried a long tradition of Greek scholarship before that time. It is known that early in the tenth century a physician who had been trained at Salerno served at the court of the King of France, and nobles came to Salerno from afar to consult the physicians at the school.

The medical school at Salerno was a lay school, primarily. The ten physicians of the faculty were paid by the students. One of the first important written works to be created there dealt with daily practices within the hospital, and set forth certain standards for the care of patients. In the eleventh century, an edition of this *Antidotarium* included prescriptions known to the ancient Greeks and some borrowed from Arab physicians. But Arab influence was felt most definitely at Salerno during the last part of the eleventh century, when Constantinus Africanus taught there. Constantinus came from Carthage on the coast of Africa. He studied medicine as a young man and made long trips to Africa and the Middle East. Later, apparently, he came to Salerno as secretary of the Duke of Salerno. There he became a professor at the medical school. Still later, he joined the Benedictine order and lived at the famous monastery at Montecassino, where he practiced his knowledge of Oriental languages by translating. He translated parts of Hippocrates and Galen from the Arabic, and he is given credit for exposing the faculty and students at Salerno to the works of their neighbors, the Arabs, in Sicily.

Early in the history of the school at Salerno a famous poem was composed which gave many of the rules of medi-

cine that had been handed down from one physician to
another since ancient times. The fact that these rules
were written in poetic style indicates one of the major
methods of transmitting knowledge in medieval times—
memorization. Writing materials were expensive and not
to be wasted on simple notes, so students and even practitioners committed their knowledge to memory. This
poem, called *Flos medicinae,* combined the principles
of the Salerno school of medicine: dietary care and simple
drugs. A number of copies of the poem were made, and
the number of stanzas varied between 350 and 3,500.
An edition published several hundred years later by
Arnold of Villanova contained 362 stanzas. Here (with
spelling changed to conform to modern usage) is the
first verse from the translation from the Latin by Sir John
Harington, published in 1607:

> The Salerno school doth by these lines impart
> All health to England's King, and doth advise
> From care his head to keep, from wrath his heart,
> Drink not much wine, sup light, and soon arise,
> When meat is gone, long sitting breedeth smart;
> And afternoon still waking keep your eyes.
> When moved you find yourself to nature's needs,
> Forbear them not, for that much danger breeds,
> Use three physicians still; first Doctor Quiet,
> Next Doctor Merryman, and Doctor Diet.

Other verses gave specific advice, as this:

> Eggs newly laid are nutritious to eat,
> And roasted rare are easy to digest.
> Fresh Gascoigne wine is good to drink with meat,
> Broth strengthens nature above all the rest.

Scientifically, Salerno came under the influence of the Arabs and prospered because of it. The study of anatomy by the dissection of animals was practiced there. Up to that time anatomy had been taught by quoting Galen, but at this medical school the teachers realized the importance of real study of anatomy. The first Italian writing on the subject of surgery originated at Salerno, so it is possible to say that in medical science progress was being made during the Middle Ages in Europe.

Generally, however, scientific progress in this period was slight before the coming of Scholasticism in the twelfth and thirteenth centuries. In many ways technology may be said to be a precursor of scientific thought and progress, thus the technology of the Dark Ages deserves considerable attention. After the fall of Rome, there was little progress in mining. When the Romans left Britain, even the technique of stonecutting fell into decay, and when the monks at Wearmouth monastery wanted to build a wall, according to the Venerable Bede, they had to cross over into Gaul to find masons, and to build their churches they imported glaziers, who were not to be found in the British Isles in the seventh century. The use of metals suffered equally after the fall of Rome, and from the third century, when the output of metals began to drop, until the ninth century, the people of Europe used old shallow mines on a disorganized basis. Improvements were not to come for some years.

In agricultural implements there was considerable improvement around the year 1000, with development of suitable plows for heavy soils. Some historians credit the barbarians with bringing to civilization the wheeled plows. Pliny noted that they had been introduced in the heavy soils of Bavaria. But the wheeled plow did not by itself solve agricultural problems, or increase the amount of land under cultivation. The moldboard, which guides the furrow and turns it over, was a far more important invention, and it dates from the eleventh century. But there were important inventions in this period, including the water mill, which, in efficient form, seems to have appeared around 500 A.D. By 1086, the Domesday Book in England listed some five thousand mills in England, or a mill for about every four hundred people.

Horses were given greater tasks in medieval times than before. The horse collar was introduced, which allowed the horse to pull far better than when yoked as an ox, and horse power replaced ox power in many areas.

The point of these inventions was to increase human productivity on the land—to make it possible for more men to do other than work to feed themselves. The rise in productivity meant that more men could work on specialties of the time, such as metals, carpentry, and building with stone. These changes came slowly, and most of them were not remarkably advanced by the eleventh century, when the flow of knowledge from the Arab world made a great impression in Europe. The earliest Oriental scientific influence in Europe is thought to be that of the Jewish doctor Sabbarai ben Abraham be Joel, who practiced medicine at Rossano in southern Italy in the middle of the tenth century. Like Constantinus Africanus in the next century, this doctor studied the sciences of the Arabs when he was captured by the Saracens. His most important work is called the *Book of Creation,* and it appeared in 946. It showed definite influences of the Arab world.

In that same century, while knowledge seeped into such places of learning as Salerno, a monk named Gerbert, who was to become Pope Sylvester II, studied in northern Spain, where Jews, Moslems, and Christians mingled as they did in southern Italy. In the middle of the eleventh century, Herman the Cripple was writing from a Benedictine abbey in Switzerland. Herman could not read Arabic, and he could not travel, but his writings showed the effects of the knowledge of the Moslem world.

From the end of the eleventh century, the writings at the medical school at Salerno began to be filled with words of Arabic origin—a certain sign of the influence being wielded by the children of Mohammed. In the eleventh, twelfth, and thirteenth centuries, as noted, translations began to come thick and fast. Gerard of Cremona worked on his translations at Toledo, as did many others in that area. In Sicily, busy men such as Eugenius of Palermo, an admiral, took to translating from the Arabic.

This infusion of knowledge brought about a basic change in the attitude of the Western world toward life in general. Until the knowledge of the ancients became generally known, thoughtful men had regarded the world as a passing fancy of God and had concentrated their efforts on the study of religion. Earliest was the attitude that science was a waste of time, and even evil. By the seventh century the Church had accepted astrology. By the eleventh century Moslem translations had brought new knowledge of astrological ideas to Europe, and so avidly did the Europeans seize on it that astrology became a major study in the West, a position it held securely until the seventeenth century. Aristotle's conception of

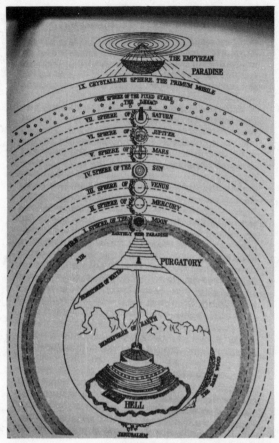

THE EMPYREAN

PARADISE

IX. CRYSTALLINE SPHERE. THE PRIMUM MOBILE

VIII. SPHERE OF THE FIXED STARS
THE ZODIAC

VII. SPHERE OF SATURN

VI. SPHERE OF JUPITER

V. SPHERE OF MARS

IV. SPHERE OF THE SUN

III. SPHERE OF VENUS

II. SPHERE OF MERCURY

I. SPHERE OF THE MOON

EARTHLY PARADISE

AIR

PURGATORY

HEMISPHERE OF WATER

HEMISPHERE OF EARTH

THE DARK WOOD

HELL

JERUSALEM

Dante's scheme of the universe, modified by Michelangelo Caetani

the universe, as made up of living beings with the heavenly bodies more noble than those of earth, was magnified and changed to a belief that the heavenly bodies directly controlled those of earth. The Christian church held that there was a life after death, that God was in control of life, and that human beings were intended to live for a long time, in which personal decisions must be made and activities chosen. Here the Church apparently saw no objection to man's reliance on astrology for direction, and because astrology made life seem simpler and more bearable, it was adapted as a guide in life.

With the thirteenth century Arabian science had traveled the length and breadth of Europe and the work and philosophy of Aristotle were becoming established, largely through the spread of universities as important parts of European life. Initially had come the church schools, then universities, such as Salerno. Later this system was broadened. There were three kinds of universities. First were the church universities, such as Paris, Oxford, and Cambridge, where students and masters formed a corporation under a chancellor. Second were civic universities, wherein students elected a rector to govern them, as at Bologna and Padua. Third were state universities, founded by a king with the approval of the Pope, as those at Naples and Salerno.

At these universities men began to question certain ideas and to think for themselves. Robert Grosseteste, a Franciscan friar, was one of these independent scholars. Another was his student, Roger Bacon, who advocated experimentation. Bacon wrote on such subjects as *optics*, in which he had studied the work of Alhazen. He wrote on many subjects, too, and finally attracted the unfavorable attention of the Pope, by whom he was punished, although mildly, for near heresy. Bacon had suggested that man would eventually build submarines, self-propelled ships, and carriages that would move on land, and flying machines. He was not the first to think so far ahead; the men of these early times were far from savages.

Grosseteste and Bacon in a way were products of an entirely new idea in the Christian world—the mendicant religious orders, whose members swore oaths of poverty, wore simple robes, and dedicated themselves to the service of God and man. Their particular order, the Franciscans, had been founded by St. Francis of Assisi, a gentle man who loved all the world and who bequeathed to his followers the study of the world.

A second religious order that was important to education was that of the Dominicans, founded by St. Dominic at Toulouse in 1215. The Dominicans became educators and students of scientific matters, but their basic aim was to conform all worldly knowledge to the necessities of religion. It would not do to have men believing the world operated in a manner different from the view held by the church fathers.

Scholasticism was an immediate outcome of the spread of Arabic translations of the works of the old Greek and Roman scholars. At its highest point Scholasticism was founded on the philosophy of Aristotle. But what an arid ground that philosophy came out upon when it was deposited in Europe! Aristotle, as we have seen, was a synthesist who gathered together the works of many previous scholars, and added his own genius to the total. In his own time he did not represent an exclusive point of view. He had set up the Lyceum in opposition to the established Academy, but the Academy did not go out of existence. Rather, it continued to flourish, and many students and scholars of merit did their work in it.

The Scholastics unfortunately did not view Aris-
totelianism as only one of several philosophies. As they
gained knowledge of this great man's ideas, they found
that his ideas fit very well with their own interpretations of nature, particularly when they read into them
what they thought they saw. The first Scholastic student
to be acquainted with the works of Aristotle was Alexander of Hales. Albertus Magnus, a Dominican, reduced
the system of Aristotle to an orderly philosophy that could
be understood in medieval times. St. Thomas Aquinas,
another Dominican, contributed new interpretations of
Aristotle that made the ancient Greek's ideas seem more
like those of the thirteenth century than those of the
fourth century before the birth of Christ. But to understand what Aquinas did, one must first understand what
he was destroying, and that, basically, was a world view
that had grown up since the fall of Rome.

As the Christian church rose it split into several divisions. The Syrians were the first to adopt a literal acceptance of Scripture, and particularly of the Book of Genesis,
which held that the earth was surrounded by water. Roman
churchmen, backed by some knowledge of scientific matters, knew the general nature of the earth and heavens
and were much more cautious in their interpretations.
But in 394 the Bishop of Tarsus, Diodorus, had attacked
those who believed in a geocentric system. A minor official of the Christian church wrote six volumes of nonsense
in which he denied all the knowledge the ancients had
gained so painstakingly. His name was Kosmas Indi-
copleustes. His works cannot be taken very seriously, for
no one really knows who he was. He denied the roundness of earth—called it a rectangular plane—and made

many other assertions of a similar character. The value of his writing is simply to show how religious fanaticism, particularly in the Christian church of the East, led men to deny all that had been learned in the past.

In Europe matters did not go quite so badly among the Christians. One cosmic view discussed by William of Conches, a Norman, was held widely in the first half of the twelfth century, just when the Scholastics were beginning to enjoy some influence. It could be called representative of pre-Scholastic thought, the culmination of the ideas of the stagnant period of the Dark Ages. In this view the earth was supposed to live in the middle of the universe, like the yolk of an egg. Outside it lay the water, like the white around the yolk, and around the water lay the air, like the skin around the egg, and outside that lay the fire, like the shell. The two temperate zones of earth were held to be habitable, but only the one known to the men of Europe was supposedly inhabited. The sun and the other heavenly bodies that could be seen to move supposedly traveled in circles about the earth.

This was the period of encyclopedists, but many of these works had gotten so far off the track of truth that their "facts" bore little resemblance to past events. For example, a book called *Image du Monde*, written in the thirteenth century, said that Ptolemy, the King of Egypt, invented clocks and various instruments and wrote several books, one of which was the *Almagest*. Its writer also noted that there were two heavens, one of which was occupied by angels, and that children could hear the celestial music as long as they retained their innocence. The book said nothing about the planetary system.

Of course, the writer had simply mixed up the Ptolemy

family of kings and the Ptolemy who was an astronomer. Still, it is significant that this ill-informed encyclopedist called Ptolemy's work by its Arabic name, *Almagest,* because it shows exactly how the real knowledge of the ancients was coming back into the West.

Scholasticism did not enter the world without a struggle. At a provincial church council in Paris in 1209 the authorities indicated their fear of the writings of the ancient heathens. They decreed that Aristotle's books on natural philosophy should not be read publicly or privately in Paris, nor might any commentaries on them be read. In 1215 this provision was added to the statutes of the University of Paris. But forty years later the Church had begun to accept Aristotle and interpret his writings in its own way. In 1254 the Aristotelian idea was solidly adopted at the University of Paris.

At Oxford University's Merton College a considerable amount of important work and study was devoted to the infant science of mechanics, predating Galileo's work and leading up to it. Also in mathematics, John Maudith, Thomas Bradwardine, and Richard of Wallingford took the sketchy trigonometry of the Arabs and from it created Western trigonometry, applying Euclid's methods of demonstration and proof. Richard of Wallingford also invented a number of instruments, among them an equatorium, to show the positions of the planets. Merton College was known at that time for its work in astronomy as well as in mathematics and mechanics.

Thomas Aquinas was the most important writer among the Scholastics. He was also the most important of the new students of Aristotle who did so much to bring the science of that ancient to Europe—and then to hold that system as the highest to which man could aspire. Thomas Aquinas, like all good churchmen, believed that divine revelation was a more important way of learning than through human reason. But unlike some of the religious men of the earlier Middle Ages, he did not scoff at human search for knowledge. He welcomed it. This was a great change. He also managed to reconcile himself to two sets of facts, two ways of finding truth. He was not disturbed by differences between Aristotle and the Bible, but took the position that both came from the same source, and that only some minor mystery prevented understanding of the difference.

Further, Thomas Aquinas added to Aristotle, where necessary. He substituted the epicycles of Hipparchus and Ptolemy for Aristotle's homocentric spheres which were supposed to explain the universe. He quoted Ptolemy's arguments about the position of the earth as center of the universe. When he had finished his work it became world famous, and the Scholastics who arose in the universities, men in search of knowledge, began to hold that there was no greater knowledge than Aristotle's. That attitude was to prove both blessing and curse in the last days of the Middle Ages.

CHAPTER **13**

The Stage for Renaissance

THE medieval period has been called one in which the human mind failed to increase the stock of knowledge and sank slowly into a low of ignorance and indifference. Most of Europe suffered from the low point around the tenth century, at the time when Arabic science was becoming highly refined. Then, with translation and the stimulus of old ideas that seemed to be new ones, European scholars began to remove their eyes from the pages of religious works and to study the world around them.

The Scholastics were bent on absorption of this ancient knowledge, often to the point of ignoring natural life around them. Thomas Aquinas was not an experimenter by nature, but he was something of an observer. The two great Franciscans, Robert Grosseteste and Roger Bacon, were better examples of what was to come in future years. Grosseteste was the Bishop of Lincoln and the Chancellor of Oxford University. He taught Roger Bacon and led him into the study of nature, but it is Bacon's contribution that is seen as a basic change in Western man's way of looking at the world.

As a Franciscan friar, Roger Bacon studied a number of the ancients in their own language and became aware that Thomas Aquinas had adapted the writings of Aristotle to the teachings of the Church. Bacon, a controversial figure who was sometimes accused of being jealous of the success of others, was intolerant of opinions he found dogmatic or foolish. He argued against the hairsplitting that characterized Scholasticism, and he argued so loudly and so long that eventually the Pope called on him for copies of all his work and placed him under the direct supervision of the heads of the order. In other words, Bacon was warned against his nonconformist ideas and watched closely.

Bacon prepared a number of books, and while they were not much honored by his own generation, they were shadows of the future. He wrote on mathematics, astronomy, astrology, mechanics, optics, alchemy, and geography. Besides prophesying inventions of the future, he predicted the way the future would unfold, and if many of his contemporaries did not heed him, he still deserves to be honored in the history of science because he helped others find the way. One of the most important statements of Bacon concerned experimentation. Without experiment, he said, nothing could be known. There were two means of acquiring knowledge, he declared, by reasoning and by experience, but while reasoning brought conclusions it did not make the conclusions certain.

If a man who had never seen a fire, said Bacon, proved by reasoning that a fire burned and destroyed, he might still not be satisfied about the properties of fire until he

Tenth-century scheme of zodiac. In the center is Christ; around Him are the signs of the zodiac assigned to the various parts of the human body

placed his hand or something else in a fire and learned by experience that fire did burn and could injure. "Reasoning does not suffice," said Bacon, "but experience does."

This was far from the usual method of thinking in that day. The rise of Scholasticism brought about an increase in universities and university education and helped pave the way for modern science, but Scholasticism was narrow and dogmatic in itself.

The three different types of universities which grew up in this pre-Renaissance period had one thing in common: all were subject to the final authority of the church fathers, in the beginning, and the struggle to free university education from the control of the Church was long and hard. At first, except in a handful of schools, the masters were clerics, because the Church almost alone in the West had kept learning alive. In all the universities the courses of study were subject to the final authority of the Pope, and the Pope chose the examiners and issued licenses to universities.

From the year 1200 on, universities began to increase in number until at the beginning of the Renaissance about 80 had been founded, 20 in Italy, about the same number in France, 14 in the German territories, and a half dozen in England, with a few others scattered elsewhere. At Paris, one of the leading universities, the curriculum consisted of the seven liberal arts, philosophy, law, and theology. The liberal arts were divided into two sections: the *trivium* and the *quadrivium*. The *trivium* consisted of grammar, rhetoric, and dialectics. The *quadrivium* consisted of arithmetic, geography, astronomy, and music. The scale of learning was arranged with liberal arts at the bottom and theology at the top.

In the beginning, universities scarcely deserved the name, if we compare them with the universities of today. At first the faculties were scattered throughout the city, as in Paris. The one uniting factor was the control of the university through the cathedral of Notre Dame. At times lectures were held in the homes of the professors of the universities. Oxford and Cambridge developed in a slightly different tradition. Special houses were built for students, where they were governed by a teacher. From this system came the organization of colleges as basic units within the university.

The rise of the universities trumpeted the ending of the Middle Ages, although the process was to be slow and painful, as the learning process always is. The inflow of ancient learning from the Arabs brought about a search by a few scholars for Greek manuscripts and original sources. But among the many scholars, until the fifteenth century, the process of learning was an attempt to discover what had happened in the past. In the case of the study of Aristotle this meant learning what the Greek had concluded nearly two thousand years before. The Scholastic leaders were of the opinion that they were "rebuilding" the philosophy of Aristotle, which they thought could handily contain the world of the fourteenth and fifteenth centuries. It was only gradually that other men realized ancient views could not be reconciled to their own, more modern times.

Many historians point to the physicists, and particularly to the students of medicine, as the men who slowly began to turn the eyes of the thoughtful toward the future. Medical men were in constant contact with nature, in the routine of their duties of treating the sick. There were, of course, Scholastic students of nature who paid more attention to the writings of the ancients than to what their eyes told them. But where the Scholasticism of the Church was not overwhelming, students of medicine began to exercise their curiosity. The medical school at the University of Padua soon became a leader in independent thought, largely through the presence of Pietro d'Abano, who studied the ancients and the Arabs, and then went on to think for himself. He was sought out by nobles and a Pope as a doctor, but as his fame increased so did the suspicion of the church fathers that his beliefs were borrowed so freely from the hated Arabs that they became anti-Christian. D'Abano was accused by the Inquisition of heresy, in 1315. He died while the case was being prepared by the Church, but in 1316 he was condemned, and his body was ordered burned after his death.

Another important student of medicine at Padua was Gentile da Foligno, who wrote a number of medical case histories which showed the practice of scientific observation rather than merely the study of the ancients. Da Foligno also dissected a human cadaver publicly at Padua. Other revolutionary ideas were being advanced elsewhere, as at Bologna, Montpellier, and Oxford. At Bologna before the end of the thirteenth century Hugh of Lucca studied practical surgery, and his son, Theodoric, maintained that the formation of pus in wounds was not necessary for healing as thirteenth-century physicians had believed. Theodoric also wrote of the use of anesthesia or narcosis, in which sponges were drenched in a narcotic and applied to the nose of the patient until he slept. Then the operation was begun. Another surgeon at Bologna, William of Saliceto, introduced the use of the knife to replace the Arab cautery. He sewed up severed nerves and noted the difference between spurting arterial blood and the steady flow of blood from the veins.

An important development of the late thirteenth and

early fourteenth centuries was the growing practice of dissecting human bodies. Until the thirteenth century most knowledge of anatomy came from the pages of Galen's books, but in later years physicians began to experiment for themselves. Male and female bodies were dissected, at Bologna, Venice, Florence, Paris, and other schools. Ordinarly the bodies used were those of executed criminals, but in 1302 when a man named Azzolino died in Bologna, and the authorities suspected that he had been poisoned, dissection of the body was ordered to discover the facts.

The first book on anatomy produced in medieval times was the work of Mondino de' Luzzi, known in Latin as Mundinus, who lectured at Bologna in the first quarter of the fourteenth century. He was the first to introduce the systematic teaching of anatomy as a part of the study of medicine, and after his book was made available the traditional method of teaching anatomy arose. Medical students were assembled in a room with the cadaver. There the teacher stood on a raised platform and held the book of Mundinus in his hand. Below him stood the man who was to perform the dissection. As the teacher read from Mundinus's text, the man with the knife illustrated on the cadaver.

The work of Mundinus became so widely accepted that after his death anyone who differed from the methods set forth in his book was suspected of evil. For three hundred years lecturers on anatomy used the book in their teaching.

In France several surgeons studied anatomy and lectured on the subject at universities, among them Guy de Chauliac, who maintained that without a knowledge of

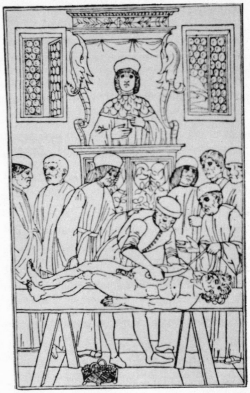

Mondino directing a dissection. From a fifteenth-century woodcut

anatomy a surgeon could do nothing. The statement was important even though it was not yet generally accepted, because it showed that a number of teachers, in spite of being suspected by the Church, recognized the fallibility of Galen and other ancients. A great physician of the period was Arnaldus de Villanova, who was born in Spain, studied at a number of medical schools in France and

Italy, and returned to Spain to practice. Later he went to Montpellier University to teach medicine. He was a physician to Pope Boniface VIII, but for some reason he became suspected of heresy and his books were outlawed by the Inquisition.

English medicine was generally behind that of the continent in this late period of the Middle Ages, but it had progressed far since the days of the Saxons, who replaced the Romans with a system of magic.

All through Europe the position of the physician and the matter of public health received a great deal of attention during the fourteenth century, which was the century of the great plague, known as the Black Death, that struck Europe. We know now that it was bubonic plague, carried by fleas that live on rats, but the medieval people of Europe did not know what it was or how it was caused. At first they did not think to look for the cause of the disease within the crowded cities, where offal was thrown in the streets and attracted rats which ran through the gutters and into the houses.

The plague apparently began in the center of Asia in the year 1333 and spread west along the trade routes. By 1346 it had passed the Middle East, entered Egypt, and crossed to Sicily and southern Italy, from which it spread north to France. In 1349 it reached Holland, Germany, England, and Poland. Two years later it reached Russia. In Florence a hundred thousand people are supposed to have died in 1348. In Venice and London the figure was higher. In Paris and Avignon the deaths totaled fifty thousand for each city. At Oxford University, where the Chancellor claimed there were thirty thousand students, the number was reduced to six thousand by this frightful disease.

In the beginning, the people of Europe blamed the plague on the heavens. The planets Saturn, Jupiter, and Mars came into conjunction on the 24th of March, 1345. So widespread was the faith in astrology that many thousands in Europe believed the conjunction was the source of the disease decimating their lands.

As time went on, the people of Europe began to understand that the plague was contagious, not carried by magic, or by the poisons of their enemies as some had believed. At the very beginning of the spread of the Black Death into Europe, Milan kept the disease outside its gates for several months by not allowing strangers to enter. Later, after the first siege, Venice forbade the entrance of any traveler suspected of having the plague. There, a special commission supervised plague precautions: guards were posted to prevent the visiting of ships, the dead could not be left on the streets, graves had to be dug to a certain depth, and special precautions were taken in the removal of bodies of those who had died of the Black Death.

In the Republic of Ragusa on the eastern side of the Adriatic Sea, authorities established a *quarentenaria,* a period of forty days in which all sailors had to remain in the fresh air before they were allowed to enter the city. This was the origin of the modern quarantine. In 1383 Marseilles established a similar practice. Other cities developed more positive measures, too, against diseases and in the preservation of public health. Houses were aired and fumigated. Furniture was taken out into the sunlight.

Vesalius dissecting among his students at Padua

The clothing of the sick was burned. Roads and water
supplies were placed under official control, and other
positive measures for public sanitation were brought into
effect. Rules were made governing the removal of corpses,
which had to be buried away from the city. Public assem-
blages were prohibited.

These actions helped prevent the spread of a number of

other diseases that scourged Europe in this period: influenza, an epidemic known as St. Anthony's fire, leprosy, and syphilis. Also, while the astrologer and the magician were still called in to help the suffering, physicians were looked to for hygienic action not covered in the works of Galen or other ancients. At Avignon, in 1348, Guy de Chauliac wrote a description of the dreadful Black Death. It came in two forms, he said. The first lasted for two months, with fever and the spitting of blood by the patient, who usually died within three days of catching the disease. After two months, the disease seemed to change its nature in Avignon. Those who contracted this second phase developed a fever, and had abscesses and carbuncles, usually under the arm or in the groin. Such patients usually died within five days. The disease was so contagious that when a member of a family contracted it, his family deserted him and fled.

In this atmosphere of fear and death the physicians of the day distinguished themselves. Protecting themselves as much as they could, they visited the sick, wearing long gloves and robes that covered them entirely. They carried sponges soaked in vinegar and treated with cloves and cinnamon, through which they inhaled each breath. In contradiction of the medieval habit of tightly closing doors and windows of the sickrooms, they insisted that such places be frequently aired and cleaned.

When the plague ended in the middle of the fourteenth century many physicians had written about it, and many cities had taken measures which were to become standard in control of that and other diseases. The plague returned toward the end of the century, but its results were not so severe.

In the fifteenth century, medicine made considerable scientific progress, in many cases because of the fright the people had suffered during the plague and the epidemics of the hundred years before. The study of anatomy became less difficult, as resistance to the dissection of human bodies decreased in the wave of Humanism that began to sweep across Europe in that century. The study of botany was increased by interest in the plant kingdom, and this led to an improvement in the collection and use of herbs and plants valuable for medicine. Toward the end of the fifteenth century the spread of printing helped all learning, including medicine, and the growth of science generally by bringing books within the range of people who had never been able to afford them before. Illustrations in such books helped immeasurably with the learning process.

At this time, another development occurred which was to leave a deep mark on the history of science. Books were sometimes written in the vulgar languages of the countrymen, and not always in Latin. Aldobrandino of Siena, for example, wrote a book about hygiene in French. Other physicians wrote in Italian. Books on herbs began to be printed not only as medical texts, but for popular use, instructing the people in the values of certain plants as medicine.

Toward the end of the fifteenth century, Pope Sixtus IV issued a bull which gave the Church's approval of the dissection of human cadavers. No longer would medical students have to practice dissection in hiding, as they sometimes did, or would the colleges be forced to resort to bribery and other dishonesties to obtain bodies for the study of anatomy. At this same time, some progressive teachers became bold enough to criticize the works of Galen and other experts of a thousand years earlier or more. However, one must not overestimate the value of what the medievalists learned from their scientific observations. They still spoke of "humors" as controlling the actions of the body in health and disease, and they misunderstood much that they saw in the dissecting rooms, especially as it concerned the heart and circulatory system. In this century a physician named Saladino de Ascoli became so displeased with the incompetence of pharmacists he knew that he prepared a book on drugs and herbs, giving ways of making compounds and preserving medicines.

During the second half of the fifteenth century the emphasis of medical teaching moved definitely away from church domination, but the general teaching was still that of the ancients. The bravery of the man who criticized Galen was notable, because most teachers did not dare to do the same. The physician who conducted a dissection was also notable, because at most universities public dissections were held only once a year or so, and then in a ceremonial atmosphere. At Bologna, in the same century, only third-year medical students were permitted to observe the dissection of a cadaver, and only a few of them at a time. It took four or five years to secure a medical license, and in some universities the applicant was obliged to swear that he would not perform operations. Such work was left for surgeons, whose rank was far lower than that of the physicians. Surgery was sometimes practiced by barbers. In England barbers and surgeons belonged to the same guild until 1745, when the surgeons split away, and all through the Christian world the differences were

great between the surgeon, who soiled his hands with operations and bloodletting, and the physician who dosed
and instructed his patients.

By the end of the fifteenth century hospitals were well
organized in Europe. The practice of medicine was in the
hands of laymen and the religious orders had nothing to
do with it. Medical schools were well organized, with
severe penalties established for those who practiced without a license, and ethical rules had been established. Medical historian Arturo Castiglioni notes: "It is at this time
that we first find a body of professional laws so adequate
and well thought out that even up to our own times it has
not been necessary to make any considerable changes."

Spectacles, or eyeglasses, the result of scientific study
of optics, were invented in these last days of medievalism.
Yet the same period saw the attempt to cure scrofula by
the laying on of hands by kings. Diet played an important
part in medieval medicine, as did incantations, amulets,
and exorcism of devils. Patients were sometimes fed
dragon's blood, fluid of frogs, and bile of vipers and snails.

An important part of the preparation for the future of
medical science came in the rise of Humanism, the belief
that man is a dignified creature who has a right to be
happy while on earth. This attitude was a complete re-
versal of the attitude of despair during the Dark Ages,
in which men suffered the discomforts of nature and sickness and told themselves that if they were lucky their
miserable days on earth would be ended and they would be
gathered into a warm, comfortable heaven.

In medicine much preparatory work had been accomplished by the end of the fifteenth century, but it was
largely only preparatory. Its value lay mostly in the plant-

ing of the seeds of change in the minds of teachers and students.

In other fields of science Roger Bacon led all others in his variety of interests, but another experimenter of importance was Pierre de Maricourt, who worked with magnetism. Alchemy was revived in Europe with the new interest in the ancients and in the translations of the scientific writings of the Arabs. Europeans learned to distill alcohol (so well that a chapter of Dominicans at Rimini was forbidden to use distilling apparatus in 1288). In 1317 Pope John XXII issued a bull forbidding the practice of alchemy because alchemists intruded upon areas reserved to the Church, which was suspicious of discussions of the "soul" properties of metals, and the search for an answer to the riddle of life as well as the manufacture of gold.

The renaissance in art and literature was beginning, and the groundwork was being laid for modern science, but science was not yet very far along by modern standards. Much had to happen. It *would* happen—quickly—in the next two centuries, but there was still much undone at the end of the fifteenth century. One important area of man's curiosity concerned the discovery of the true nature of the earth. Henry the Navigator was one of the major figures in this revival of interest in geography. Others were Columbus, Vasco da Gama, Amerigo Vespucci, and Ferdinand Magellan. Such men, daring to sail out of sight of land, conquered the oceans and learned the true size and shape of their earth. Throughout the known world interest in education became greater than it had been for a thousand years.

In the fourteenth century William of Ockham at Oxford

University had suggested that Thomas Aquinas was not necessarily correct in his contention that the heavenly spheres moved and that this was proof of the existence of God simply because somebody had to move them.

William of Ockham said that all that had been needed was an original push from somewhere. This was the "impetus theory," originally offered by John Philoponus, the Alexandrian, and transmitted to Europe by the Arabs. The impetus theory also developed at Paris, where Jean Buridan denied that angels propelled the heavenly bodies on their courses as the new Aristotelians believed. Later at Paris, Albert of Saxony added to the theory, and Nicolas Oresme carried it further in his studies of mathematics. He decided that the earth revolved on its own axis, and that the heavens did not move every day. He believed that the spin of the earth had been created once and would continue forever because there was no resistance to it.

These were complex ideas. A few of the impetus theorists also believed that the universe might be infinite, and that other worlds such as the one they knew might exist elsewhere in space. Nicholas of Cusa, a bishop in the Tyrol region in 1450, accepted this explanation. But most churchmen and most scholars accepted the earlier theories of Aristotle as revised and handed down by Thomas Aquinas. To them there was only one universe, based on the earth. The earth lay motionless at the center of the universe and was surrounded by celestial spheres of increasing perfection. These spheres were kept in motion by angels. This was the general belief of educated men at the end of the medieval period, on the eve of the dawn of the movement that would develop swiftly into modern science.

CHAPTER 1 For this chapter I drew heavily on the following books: *A History of Science, Ancient Science Through the Golden Age of Greece*, by George Sarton. Professor Sarton's placement of the civilizations of the Fertile Crescent and that of Egypt, in point of importance to the West, does not agree with all other historians of science, but his description of the scientific efforts of the civilizations known altogether as Babylonian is succinct and pointed. I also used Joseph Campbell's *Oriental Mythology*, not a scientific history or study in the usual sense, but a valuable adjunct to anyone who wishes to pursue the study of the Fertile Crescent's civilizations. *Eastern Science*, by H. J. J. Winter, is a small book (114 pages including index) but it is indispensable for the orientation of dates, places, and people, and its capsulization of scientific affairs is helpful to any young student. Medicine in the Fertile Crescent is treated by Sarton, by Charles Singer and E. Ashworth Underwood in their memorable *A Short History of Medicine*, and in Warren R. Dawson's first volume of the Clio Medica series of primers on medical history *The Beginnings, Egypt and Assyria*. For an orientation on the changes in the approach to the history of science the book *Toward Modern Science*, Volume I, *Studies in Ancient and Medieval Science*, contains some helpful guideposts as does Derek J. de Solla Price's *Science Since Babylon*.

CHAPTER 2 Most of the modern material relative to the history of science in China is contained in the massive study of *Science and Civilization in China* by Joseph Needham, a projected seven-volume work of which four volumes have now been published. It is the single most authoritative work on the subject in the English language. Volume III is probably the most valuable for young students who seek further specific information on Chinese science. Needham and Lu Gwei-Djen published an article on preventive medicine and hygiene in Ancient China in the *Journal of the History of Medicine and Allied Sciences,* the quarterly publication of the Department of the History of Science and Medicine of Yale University. As Needham notes many times in his work, there are many areas of Oriental history of science and medicine in which there is virtually no knowledge available to Westerners—at least in English or any other Western language. It is a beckoning field for any young person who is interested in both the challenge and opportunity of ancient history.

CHAPTER 3 George Sarton's *History of Science* was foundation reading for this chapter. He begins his work with a study of Egyptian science, rather than Babylonian, and uses the experience of the ancient people of the Nile to point up the growth of science, as science, in the worlds of the Middle East. Winter's *Eastern Science* was again valuable, as was Dawson's work on *Medicine in Egypt.* Soloman Gandz's discussion of Babylonian and Egyptian mathematics in *Toward Modern Science* was helpful, and O. E. Neugebauer's chapter on "Exact Science in Antiquity" was equally valuable in raising questions as to why things happened as they did, and in suggesting some answers. Charles Singer and a number of others edited a classic *History of Technology* which was published in 1954. Volume I of this work gives a complete picture of the trend of human accomplishment from times far beyond the knowledge of history to the end of the ancient empires. This work does not deal heavily with the Far East's development of technology, but with that of the Middle East and European worlds, with some references to the Indus civilization and some to China.

CHAPTER 4 Again, George Sarton's *History of Science,* Volume I, was a basic source for information for this chapter. To gain a feeling for the magnificence of these ancient civilizations there is much to be said for reading Herodotus, the first historian whose work is meaningful to the Western world. This may be a bit hard going for young adults, but if Book One of *The Histories* can hold attention for a hundred pages, the idea will come through. Other valuable sources for this chapter included Volume I of *History of Technology* by Singer and others, J. L. E. Dreyer's *History of Astronomy* from Thales to Kepler, and *Theories of the Universe,* edited by Milton K. Munitz.

CHAPTER 5 In addition to Professor Sarton's work, I consulted Giorgio de Santillana's *The Origins of Scientific Thought* in my study of the science of Ionia. Stephen F. Mason's *History of the Sciences* gives a quick look at this period in a very brief space. J. L. E. Dreyer gives more detail about astronomy and views of the universe for those who care to be more technical. F. M. Cornford's chapter on Ionian cosmography would be fairly difficult for a young person, but instructive. Arturo Castiglioni's *History of Medicine* gives a good picture of the beginning of medical science in Greece.

CHAPTER 6 Professor Sarton's *History of Science*, Stephen Mason's *History of Science*, and Professor Castiglioni's *History of Medicine* are basic sources here. Also de Santillana has interesting, if difficult, discussions of ideas. The works of Aristotle also are rather difficult for young readers, but many of them are available in translation.

CHAPTER 7 J. L. E. Dreyer's *History of Astronomy* tells much about the state of science in Alexandria. Professor Sarton's *History of Science*, Volume II, is invaluable for discussion of this period. Stephen Mason's brief survey gives a general picture, and both Charles Singer and Arturo Castiglioni deal with the medicine of this period in some detail.

CHAPTER 8 The basic sources for this chapter are again Professor Sarton's Volume II, of *A History of Science*, and Arturo Castiglioni's *History of Medicine*. Benjamin Farrington's *Science in Antiquity* is valuable for another look at the Alexandrians, as is Stephen Mason's *History of the Sciences*. A very interesting book for young readers here is *Moments of Discovery*, Volume I, called *The Origins of Science*, edited by George Schwartz and Philip W. Bishop. It contains excerpts from the actual words of a number of the greats of this and other periods in the development of early science: such men as Ptolemy, Galen, Archimedes, Aristotle, Eratosthenes. Its excerpts are short and easy to read.

CHAPTER 9 *History of Technology*, Volume II, is valuable here for an understanding of the technical improvements the Romans were able to make in various practices. Charles Singer's *History of Scientific Ideas to 1900* is good reading for an understanding of the philosophy of the Romans. So is the chapter in his *From Magic to Science*, which deals with Rome. Arturo Castiglioni's study of medicine and hospitalization in Rome was used, from his *History of Medicine*.

CHAPTER 10 Philip K. Hitti's *History of the Arabs* is very good background for an understanding of the development of the Arab civilization in both East and West. It is not quite so useful in terms of understanding the scientific development. H. J. J. Winter's *Eastern Science* is most helpful in that regard, although it is very brief. J. L. E. Dreyer discusses the Arab astronomers at some length in his *History of Astronomy*. There is a French history, *La Science Arabe* by Aldo Mieli, for those who might read freely in that language.

CHAPTER 11 Again, Philip Hitti's *History of the Arabs* is valuable in setting the scene, and in helping to understand what happened in Spain and North Africa during this period. Other sources are the same as in Chapter Ten. In addition, Castiglioni's *History of Medicine* deals at some length with the decline of Arabian medicine and its teaching and practice.

CHAPTER 12 The sources used for this chapter were A. C. Crombie's *Medieval and Early Modern Science,* Volume I, Castiglioni's *History of Medicine,* Mason's *History of the Sciences,* and various other brief references. Schwartz and Bishop's *Origins of Science* contains some excellent brief notes on the period, given under the names of the men involved. J. L. E. Dreyer's *History of Astronomy* gives a picture of the way the people of the Middle Ages looked at life and the heavens. *Theories of the Universe* by Milton Munitz provides a good brief presentation of the work of Lucretius.

CHAPTER 13 Charles Singer's *History of Scientific Ideas to 1900* and his *From Magic to Science* are basic sources for this chapter on the last days of the medievalists. Also, George Sarton's *Six Wings,* a study of men of science in the Renaissance, gives a good background to this pre-Renaissance period (as far as science is concerned). Schwartz and Bishop's *Moments of Discovery,* Volume I, offers a good picture of Roger Bacon, of Aristotle and of Galen. They were the most important figures in the medieval period, although long dead, and the problem was to shake off their dead hands. Stephen Mason again gives a briefer treatment.

I owe an enormous debt to Derek J. de Solla Price, Chairman of the Department of History of Science at Yale University. In the beginning, he steered me to bibliography. In the middle he corrected my errors in approach. In the end, he read the entire manuscript. He bears no responsibility for any errors in emphasis or in fact that may remain, but if there is scholarly value in an approach to history of science by a nonscientific member of the literary community, Dr. Price is responsible for the value of this book.

I am also indebted to a number of persons, teachers, and others, who have read portions of the manuscript, including Philip Downes of the Department of History at Kent School, and several faculty members at Indian Mountain School, Lakeville, Connecticut. My wife, Olga Hoyt, assisted in reading and editing, as did Robert Hill, my editor. Mrs. Eunice Soule typed the manuscript.

Index